THE  TIMES

Cryptic
Crossword

Book 1

**Test yourself with 80 general-knowledge
crosswords from times2**

Published in 2000 by Times Books

HarperCollins Publishers
Westerhill Road
Bishopbriggs
Glasgow G64 2QT

www.harpercollins.co.uk
Visit the book lover's website

Reprint 10 9 8 7 6 5 4

The Times is a registered trademark of
Times Newspapers Ltd

ISBN 978-0-00-710833-6

British Library Cataloguing in Publication Data
A catalogue record for this book is available from the British Library.

Thank you to David Akenhead

Typeset in Great Britain by Davidson Pre-Press Graphics Ltd, Glasgow G3

Printed and bound in Great Britain by Clays Ltd, St Ives plc.

INTRODUCTION

The second crossword in this collection, published on 14 January 1998, celebrated the centenary of the death of Lewis Carroll, who doubtlessly would have excelled as a composer of cryptic crosswords had the form been invented in his lifetime. Like many Victorians, he enjoyed finding apposite anagrams, such as Flit on, cheering angel (8,11).

Another of his ingenious challenges was to rearrange the letters of the following sentence into one word: Nor do we. Like Queen Victoria herself, he composed many acrostics – lines of verse in which the first letters spelt out words. Above all, he delighted in puns; the description of "The Hunting of the Snark" as "An Agony, in Eight Fits" puns on "fit", an archaic word for "canto".

Other forms of word puzzles were his own invention. In "Doublets", one word has to be transformed into another through a chain of words each differing from its predecessor by only one letter. Thus HEAD can become TAIL via HEAL, TEAL, TELL, TALL – can you change TEARS into SMILE in the same fashion?

Crossword 56 was also topical and thematic, since it coincided with the Mind Sports Olympiad, referring to many of the games included in that event. Indeed, bridge and chess, in particular, feature directly or indirectly in many of our clues.

Further, to solve one of the clues in Crossword 30, you need to be aware that it appeared on 30 April.

I'm writing from California where I recently returned to full-time academic life, at San Diego State University. In this career, I also find Lewis Carroll had remarkable insights to offer, in particular into the nature of language in relation to mathematics.

The crosswords in the book appeared in *The Times* in 1998.

Brian Greer
Crossword Editor of *The Times*, 1995–2000

(Answers: Florence Nightingale, one word, TEARS, SEARS, STARS, STARE, STALE, STILE, SMILE (for example)).

A Beginner's Guide to *The Times* Crossword

Across

1 High-flier ruined by exposure in Sun (6)
5 Nonconformist churchman's back I protected from rain (8)
9 Opposition is hesitant to reform (10)
10 Arranger selecting odd pieces for composer (4)
11 Frosty spell in unfriendly game (4,4)
12 Characteristic tone in old instrument cut short (6)
13 Charge for conversion as gas is offered, initially (4)
15 Call artist a venomous creature (8)
18 Strange sort of small house? Indeed, it was (8)
19 Absence of authorisation for retreat (4)
21 Was mistress under stress? Sounds like it (6)
23 Specify drink – same again? (8)
25 Architect leaves sewer after fall (4)
26 Like a resistance force made up without ringleader (10)
27 American statesman noted for his Canterbury relation (8)
28 For example, miss a run (6)

Down

2 Censor accepts new section in poem (5)
3 They make up shower curtains artist at home put up (9)
4 "A man" finally solved her cryptic puzzle (6)
5 Maiden is under arrest? Just the opposite – that's an error (15)
6 One making late appearance (it's in a TV broadcast) (8)
7 Raise millions to modernise the forces (5)
8 Singer, no pro, gets lot wrong (9)
14 One sort of bird – and another right outside (9)
16 Leaves without the slightest difficulty (5,4)
17 Small meal? It's hard to say (8)
20 Fine Italian instruments you love in Rome (6)
22 Involved in begging, a minor? (5)
24 One in exaltation turned up round a village (5)

Notes

Across

1 ICARUS The whole clue is a cryptic definition, and has nothing to do with a tabloid scandal about a successful person. Icarus and his father Daedalus made wings to escape from Crete but Icarus flew too high and the wax securing his wings melted in the sun's rays, so he fell to his death.

5 MAVERICK = nonconformist. The rest works like an algebraic equation, thus: VER (= churchman's back) + I inside MACK (i.e. protected from rain).

9 ANTITHESIS = opposition. Anagram of IS HESITANT (indicator: to reform).

10 ARNE = composer (Thomas Arne, 1710-1778). More unusual clue type instructing solver to select odd letters (pieces) of ArRaNgEr.

11 COLD SNAP = frosty spell. Combination of COLD (= unfriendly) + SNAP (= game).

12 TIMBRE = characteristic tone. Timbrel (old instrument) is cut short.

13 AGIO = charge for conversion (when changing money). First letters (indicator: initially) of As Gas Is Offered.

15 RINGHALS = a venomous creature (large spitting cobra). Combination of RING (call) + HALS (artist).

18 FORSOOTH = indeed (note that "it was" points to the word being archaic). Anagram: SORT OF HO (ho. = small house, i.e. abbreviation) (indicator: strange).

19 NOOK = retreat. Absence of authorisation = NO OK.

21 TAUGHT = was mistress. Homophone of taut = under stress (indicator: sounds like it).

23 NAMESAKE = same again (somewhat cryptic definition signalled by question mark). Combination of NAME (specify) + SAKE (drink).

25 Two definitions. ADAM = architect/ADAM = leaves sewer after fall (Adam and Eve sewed fig-leaves to make aprons).

26 FRICTIONAL = like a resistance force. FICTIONAL (= made up) outside (without) R (= ringleader).

27 Two definitions. FRANKLIN = American statesman (Benjamin Franklin, 1706-1790/FRANKLIN = noted for his Canterbury relation. (Franklin's Tale is one of the Canterbury Tales).

28 Two definitions. SINGLE = for example, miss (i.e. an unmarried person)/SINGLE = a run.

DOWN

2 CANTO = section in poem. CATO = censor (Marcus Porcius Cato, elected censor in 184, famous for his zeal in that capacity), contains (accepts) N = new.

3 RAINDROPS = they make up shower. DROPS = curtains, with RA = artist) + IN (= at home) on top (put up).

4 The whole clue is a cryptic definition. The SPHINX was a female monster inhabiting the district around Thebes, who set the riddle "What animal walks on four legs in the morning, two at noon, and three in the evening?". Oedipus finally provided the answer "A man", who crawls as a baby, walks upright in mid-life, and with the aid of a stick in old age.

5 MISAPPREHENSION = an error. M (= maiden) + IS on top of (under? Just the opposite) APPREHENSION (= arrest).

6 VISITANT = one making late appearance (a visitant is a ghost, i.e. late = dead person). Anagram: IT'S IN A TV (indicator: broadcast).

7 REARM = modernise the forces. Combination of REAR (= raise) + M (= millions, abbreviation).

8 CONTRALTO = singer. Combination of CONTRA (= no pro) + anagram of LOT (indicator: wrong).

14 GOOSANDER = one sort of bird. AND with GOOSE (= another (bird)) + R (= right, abbreviation) outside.

16 Two definitions. HANDS DOWN = leaves (i.e. bequeaths)/HANDS DOWN = without the slightest difficulty.

17 Two definitions. MOUTHFUL = small meal/MOUTHFUL = it's hard to say.

20 Two definitions. AMATIS = fine Italian instruments (plural of Amati)/AMATIS = you love in Rome (amo, amas, amat, amamus, amatis ...)

22 The whole clue acts both as a definition (GAMIN is a street urchin who might be involved in begging) and hidden clue – begginG A MINor (indicator: involved in).

24 KRAAL = village. LARK (= one in exaltation, exaltation being the collective noun for larks) inverted (turned up), containing (round) A.

THE PUZZLES

1

ACROSS

1 Adjourned for some wine (4)
3 Academic stream is beside itself (4)
6 Add a little terse advice to convertible driver in rain? (3,2)
10 Red nose, perhaps, that Continental got in fight (7)
11 (For course) Q: Where did Charles hide after Worcester? (7)
12 Approval given by merry socialist in speech (4,5)
13 Verse of *Abide with Me*, say, cut short in divinity lesson (5)
14 Scholar took exam, securing first place (6)
16 Conductor's turn with part of the orchestra (8)
18 Shot in two parts of body (8)
19 Break in bay (6)
22 Shortly about to run off without paying for this orange (5)
23 Alert goalkeeper may dive thus (2,3,4)
25 Filled with enthusiasm, return to log support (7)
26 One holds one's breath – it may go up (7)
27 Spencer jacket ultimately distinctive in style (5)
28 Reduce intake for legislative assembly (4)
29 Labour, generally, having it in for press? (4)

DOWN

1 Dressed in frills, Elizabeth Bennet initially had cold shoulders (7)
2 Brains are needed in this case (5)
4 Appeal to deflect god (6)
5 Sudden guess that produces negative result (8)
6 Urgent bid to reconstruct city hence protest letters, reputedly (9,5)
7 Non-exclusive way to communicate official policy (5,4)
8 As payment for part of chapter, turn in advance? (7)
9 Failure to relax, as result of driving compulsion? (7,7)
15 Intelligent, omitting line in travel document? The other way round (4,5)
17 Die clutching neck filled with blood (8)
18 Gain advantage, having been out to attack (7)
20 Justice of the Peace (7)
21 Famous birthplace definitely established (6)
24 Acceptable in European city, being head-over-heels in it? (5)

ACROSS

1 Knight among more cult characters turned out a sad creature (4,6)
6 Piece of card (4)
10 He came to a dreadful end, in agony (5)
11 Any recent novel writer has one today (9)
12 Gave evidence in trial, one launched after Queen's loss (9)
13 Bill lacking in power of speech (5)
14 One turning into a pig on the way? (4,3)
15 Argued in court quietly, like old-fashioned type (7)
17 In sorry state, is lad in mess? Off with their heads! (7)
19 Thanks to *Through the Looking-Glass*, initially, Queen's seen as gossip (7)
21 Some opera's said to be very musical (5)
23 Quiet tear about farewell – not unusual (9)
24 Regularly walk and run – it shows odd behaviour (5,4)
25 Girl not reflecting and plunging into adventures (5)
26 Repeatedly act as race organiser (4)
27 Country looking fantastic visited after fall (10)

DOWN

1 Nameless horrible creature catching Boots, initially a member of the gang (7)
2 Support for a growing girl's need (4,5)
3 Girl hushed Kitty, endlessly shaken? It's sweet (7,7)
4 Shaking violently following wild creature – no end of quest (7)
5 Joined with king going in a file (5,2)
7 I run with a queen, one inhabitant of divided land? (5)
8 County Nell and Edward reached at last (7)
9 Powerlessly falling in earth, I have a peculiar resistance (7-4-3)
16 A really good time to produce TV broadcast with 25 (5,4)
17 Hit suddenly distributes cards, going up about two metres (7)
18 Noted female, thoroughly wet, had a race – with duck (7)
19 Laughed to observe next tea being announced (3-4)
20 Take steps again to enjoy book afresh – about time (7)
22 Queen gave off about such a small amount of evidence? (5)

ACROSS

1 Conceited youngster, a future skipper, possibly (4)
3 Water very quietly absorbed in part of body (5,5)
10 Promotion of number one (4-11)
11 A barrier to progress for some races (8)
12 One watched for a shot that delights a golfer (6)
14 Wade across one? Hardly! (5)
16 Reprimand from oriental king tolerated (7-2)
18 One person's tale is inaccurate about female politician (4,5)
19 No longer taxes people up North (5)
20 Mouse taken to guy (6)
22 Fellow's agitation describing dons (8)
26 It's said to be a careless error (4,2,3,6)
27 Book individual after arrest, finding part of skeleton (10)
28 Characters in front of queue, say, in dominant position (4)

DOWN

1 The type who bothers with duck sauce (5)
2 Eliminate European side at Lord's (6,3)
4 Liberal university in commitment that distributes power (10)
5 Times supporting a chap such as Douglas? (4)
6 Drinks provided in wild parties (9)
7 Fraudulent type raised charges by minimal amount (5)
8 Seen to run off between you and me (5,4)
9 Facts making American a little upset (4)
13 Disc that's likely to be hit soon after launch (4,6)
14 The airs that people put on! (4,5)
15 Ancient intriguing led to her death (9)
17 Model of chivalry pronounced the latest word? (9)
21 Hot and sick after getting cold like this (5)
23 Sort of memory that follows piano concert (4)
24 Penny each, possibly (5)
25 Objections raised in short piece (4)

4

ACROSS

1 Contract that's set up between banks? (7)
5 One river or another – to another returned (7)
9 Stories of Italian love or of French romance, possibly (9)
10 Disc made of iron used in combat (5)
11 Friend in fur not getting chill (5)
12 Outstanding return for county's brilliant star (9)
14 Book that's good, but not first edition? (7,7)
17 Change for better infernal nuisance causing embarrassment (6,8)
21 As a rule, not many are involved in it (9)
23 It makes sense to take aim (5)
24 Could be worse off as a farm worker (5)
25 Co-partner ruined, on the other hand (3,6)
26 With method arranged, carried out ambush (7)
27 Dog appears to eat into fish (7)

DOWN

1 Reckon court must put one inside as fanatic (6)
2 Admit set is incomplete (7)
3 Restrict the flow of people's expression of anger (9)
4 One presenting picture so awful about rise of EC? (11)
5 Quarter of a pint in beer container (3)
6 Keep out of ghetto, we recommend (5)
7 As if I'm distressed about old criminals! (7)
8 Conceals the end (8)
13 Little money clear person comes up with in this (7,4)
15 Mental confusion, losing head in violent downpour (9)
16 Was no safety device put up for this cutting tool? (5,3)
18 Beautiful road a driver doesn't want to leave (7)
19 Boat for which portage is less of a problem? (7)
20 Collected maps on time, in the end (2,4)
22 A case ended prematurely in these courts (5)
25 Flat sheets of paper (3)

5

ACROSS

1 War banished from English town or one in Scotland (4)
3 Show compassion, and be able to follow suit, perhaps (4,1,5)
9 Look at some bimbo gleefully? (4)
10 House appears to shake, note (10)
12 Agreement whereby pet's restricted on rope (9)
13 Facility left for support of artistic effort (5)
14 One produces shares for consumers in joint operation (7,5)
18 It indicates a reference showing how to make a pair of stilettos? (6,6)
21 Controlling current cricket sides (2-3)
22 Assess performance of stroke on the river (4-5)
24 Charming company who had to leave early (10)
25 Told to deliver trunk (4)
26 I examine two cardinal points in new order for recruits (10)
27 Modern copper on beat's seen the light (4)

DOWN

1 Turn up and bowl first in the game (8)
2 Master preparing courses shows such skill (8)
4 Having more points each (5)
5 It's all there is (9)
6 Does one have a slim chance of holding up a casino? (5,2,5)
7 Make suggestion I'd save to be reviewed (6)
8 Turned this creature the other way up (6)
11 Disastrous sequence of events, after a knock-on? (6,6)
15 Start to risk cash with small northern negotiator (2-7)
16 British governor general (8)
17 Suddenly stop riding? Time to get your skates on! (6-2)
19 Hunting call making the majority of you sick, possibly (6)
20 Do I find a good deal useful as a club member? (6)
23 Sort out the problem of crack (5)

6

ACROSS

1 Run in a straight line (6)
4 Continental community still over the moon (8)
10 Fat cat apt to curl in a strange way (9)
11 Some meat enjoyed like this? (5)
12 Leftover old insecticide overcomes people (7)
13 Followers always holding one back (7)
14 Try something desperate – as greedy suckers do? (6,2,6)
19 Sexy beauty with part to play in historical record (6,8)
21 Having completed short time in firm (7)
24 Catch unknown creature – a parrot (7)
26 Liquor is found inside part of supermarket (5)
27 In bad-tempered case, I am willing to appear as witness (9)
28 Choke – one of car's controls (8)
29 Soldier discovering fish by a river (6)

DOWN

1 Heartlessly pay dole in new way – spread out (6)
2 Song sequence about love put off (9)
3 Clubs get beaten in the end (5)
5 React violently to pander (5)
6 Country's temperature the man reports (3,6)
7 Bird – an enormous creature (5)
8 Talk? Just the opposite (8)
9 Fancy needlework covering tail of shirt (8)
15 Aggressive exchange you reported fast (9)
16 Actors of limited range may be of two sorts (8)
17 Wicked actor somehow promises to settle scores (9)
18 Steal Jack's territory (8)
20 The old leading man comes around – he shows persistence (6)
22 One gets up part of flight (5)
23 Enable old husband to get put up in accommodation (5)
25 Soldier, without fuel, sent North on horse (5)

ACROSS

1 Plan to have no end of peace in this cathedral (8)
6 A lefty's revolutionary allegiance (6)
9 Supported rail and put in a line, in transport deal (10)
10 Star reflected in river (4)
11 Delightful person who entertains angelic bunch (8,4)
13 One captured by Spain, calamitously (4)
14 Where missile is pointed (4-4)
17 Way in which infantrymen strike gently, then hard (8)
18 Spread a little butter to end of slice (4)
20 Chap's chortling – it's killing (12)
23 Trollope's Irish member and another European (4)
24 Manager introduces band with top-class amplifier? (7,3)
25 Cage bird initially popular (6)
26 Worry and hang about, showing sign of anxiety (8)

DOWN

2 Old banger costing little that doesn't start (4)
3 Hooligan, thrown out, goes up the wall (9)
4 Tree rodent seen on bark (6)
5 Unreliable person – not to be found lurking in Ireland? (5,2,3,5)
6 Extremely poor payment poet's fortunate to get (8)
7 Embarrass, joining a party (5)
8 One's part in compilation of ten centuries? (10)
12 Being shot away? (2,8)
15 Protective cover for book (9)
16 Revolutionary acquires aristocratic title in the long run (8)
19 Blow in the band (6)
21 As Anglican, depressed by man's nature (5)
22 Sign a top rugby player (4)

8

ACROSS

1 Expert injecting horse in pain (4)
3 Schoolmaster's not hard-hearted as employer (4)
6 Father has to admit giving a dirty look (5)
10 Large animal in stream in Indian territory (7)
11 Way round hostile defensive bulge (7)
12 Topping loaf consumed by creature (9)
13 Ring route repaired (5)
14 I, for one, may be heard making this affirmation (6)
16 Victoria, for example, having time at home with Albert (8)
18 He rooted for reform, being a Roosevelt (8)
19 Drop into court in recess (6)
22 Callas, say, making mark with operatic performance (5)
23 Many an Anglo-Saxon runner initially needed a drink (9)
25 The first fruit peeled, we hear, at St. Clement's (7)
26 List that's including Times, possibly (7)
27 Person taking shot is less forward (5)
28 Go down to find place where vessels get washed up (4)
29 Dishonest grass (4)

DOWN

1 School subject a learner, for example, gets up with support (7)
2 Spartan king in a muddle (5)
4 Constant interference (6)
5 Surrendered, game being up without warning (8)
6 Shadow M? It's just a game (6-2-6)
7 Subtle implications arising from Nero's vote (9)
8 Illegitimate type of selection (7)
9 Hide with Dirk – it's to do with espionage (5-3-6)
15 Such dishes get a warm reception (4-5)
17 Buildings in the grounds (8)
18 Rough girls damaging my boots (7)
20 Only just touching a chap with sunburn (7)
21 Flag-officer? (6)
24 Stomach something ridiculous (5)

9

ACROSS

1 Tribute one in PR agency organised (9)
6 Plant that is cut by doctor died (5)
9 One hoarding two grand in back tax (7)
10 Consider a description of what happened (7)
11 Eccentric with old hat seen about (5)
12 One who arranges or, alternatively, a singer (9)
13 Live English concerts initially associated with Henry Wood (5)
14 Problem choppers might have fixing old, old hatchet (9)
17 Withdraws claws (9)
18 Best? Yes and no (5)
19 A nasty striver – one pushing in? (9)
22 This is a likely source for fibre (5)
24 Novel from Virginia or a place in Florida (7)
25 Woman being contrary about awfully good witticism (7)
26 Girl of three months, the first (5)
27 Is allowed to pick this blossom? (9)

DOWN

1 Horse pulled beer round (5)
2 Late shifts, perhaps (9)
3 Ammunition found in rubbish heaps going off (9)
4 Having had the wind up, manage to survive (4,3,3,5)
5 Operation in theatre, in new surroundings (6,2,7)
6 Yank's jailed coming from Peru, once (5)
7 Objections about love matches (5)
8 Pour cold water on fellow cleaner (9)
13 Steps taken to manage a star (5,4)
15 Turtle will bask here at first when at sea (9)
16 Opener in county's team (9)
20 Sovereign measure (5)
21 Old-fashioned record producer (5)
23 Less convincing work by Debussy (5)

10

ACROSS

1 Green's the shade for this rock (9)
6 Appear unexpectedly to be pawn ahead (3,2)
9 Bird getting stronger, gaining weight (7)
10 Account for Times appearing in English flat (7)
11 Is it odd of me to join this game? (5)
12 Lacking a match, with no pair, we hear, in love (9)
13 What makes a powerful body, or a heavenly one (8)
15 Given money to eat (4)
19 The French backs have a name for it? (4)
20 Provide care in short time, nurse having lost her head (8)
23 Advertisement about time for showing up poor linesman (9)
24 Sort of fund liable to melt away? (5)
26 Start to lose one's temper (4,3)
27 From which potential soldiers shoot (7)
28 Wine initially tasting satisfactory (5)
29 Clear, using special axe on tree (9)

DOWN

1 Relatively unimportant action the army is in, but not RAF (5,4)
2 A precept for Gorky, say (5)
3 Dashing spray hid the location of launches (8)
4 Material for dress – and there's no end of wild parties coming round (8)
5 Cast off, following this direction (6)
6 Common lacks centrepiece – a tree (6)
7 Position fitting beneficiaries of patronage exactly! (9)
8 Piece of glass left in section of door (5)
14 Distinctive sign to invest in sterling, perhaps? (9)
16 One's not fancied getting run in black stockings (4,5)
17 Harte put in agonised toil to create book (8)
18 Room for fighter with arrogance to step out (8)
21 Flier eating chop and banger (6)
22 Have trouble breathing? Fine, take steps to get round it (6)
23 Guide one into story (5)
25 Uncompromising politician shows some deceitful traits (5)

ACROSS

1 Surreptitious way to get Cockney well (8)
5 Colonialist that used to have colossal statue (6)
9 Warning: name to be used as spelled for legal purposes (8)
10 Secret animal in this labyrinth? Just the opposite (6)
12 Unaided battle to secure plant (8,4)
15 Decisively defeats opposition party on the right (5)
16 Treasury stars he's brought in (9)
18 Nothing needed at table except this bread? (9)
19 Store has incomplete seal (5)
20 Imposed diet or non-civil assembly (5,7)
24 Modest cover is revived? (6)
25 Brought back to conscious state (8)
26 Very quick delivery arriving on foot, perhaps (6)
27 Taking pledge – eighteen, of course? (8)

DOWN

1 Like this, paper is easy to cut (4)
2 Noble organ loft frequently abandoned (4)
3 Sole, tuna, and tail of whiting cooked as seafood (9)
4 Repeat prescription that covers pet (4,2,3,3)
6 Sun god's burden – must banish cold (5)
7 Child denied treat might produce desired answer (2,3,5)
8 Celebrated girls given light protection (10)
11 Spectacular way to learn history, in two senses (3,2,7)
13 One spotted next to green room, daydreaming (5,5)
14 Like dismissed monk, not working (3,2,5)
17 Die in a limited rising (9)
21 Put these people on drug? That's the idea (5)
22 Part of ship made of very immature oak? (4)
23 PM once announced such a lot of changes (4)

12

ACROSS

1 Herb a little woman found in the grass (8)
6 Almost provide complete contents for short book of pictures (6)
9 Former king suffering setback at Salamis, initially (6)
10 Many high-flyers get into this other type of crossword – and put a spurt on (5,3)
11 One trying to stop fighting of turbulent marrieds (8)
12 New missile contract (6)
13 Noise of engine, entering Victoria turned low (5)
14 Block that's part of prison? Not according to Lovelace (9)
17 It's terrible to evict drunk, but that's an order (9)
19 Modest grade got by girl in form (5)
22 Writer departs with a letter for Corinthians (6)
23 Is this clock incapable of striking one? (8)
24 Fare from India – fellow returned it with thanks (8)
25 Indication of constant pressure is nothing to lawyers (6)
26 A tint I developed for red hair (6)
27 Mean American smashed advertisement about Western (8)

DOWN

2 Place of work the French set up that's used in art, especially (7)
3 Times going into project with a stance put together (9)
4 Pick up a summary (6)
5 It may result in time being ten to two, say (8,7)
6 Iron skirt and edges of negligee suitable for woman (8)
7 Turned up stuff on whale in island (7)
8 Sheep shelters found round South-West, over the hill here? (9)
13 One food store caught in check, in other words (9)
15 Protest by workers about Jack's informal contact with public (9)
16 Produce order, say, to impose restrictions (8)
18 Man appearing ragged in torn piece of cloth (7)
20 Composer of some crosswords met an aficionado (7)
21 New shoot appears about then (6)

13

ACROSS

1 Character with whom it's rash to play poker, for a start (4-5)
6 Jazz work broadcaster half-heartedly introduced (5)
9 A herb gardener's first planted in row (5)
10 Kowtowing to get honour, in case that's corrupt (9)
11 Reserve gets point, going on pitch (7)
12 Oval ball rebounds in various directions (7)
13 Finally, a certain envelope for me by way of bonus (3,4,7)
17 Extremely restrained, but it covered a great deal of ground (14)
21 Unkempt hair finally taken off (7)
23 Child teacher abandoned in capital, a wicked city (7)
25 Excess population proves disastrously harmful (9)
26 Party-goer in right state (5)
27 Rejected dictionary word suggesting alternative for 28, say (5)
28 Punch, for example, meets with tolerance in rough-and-tumble (9)

DOWN

1 Elegant clothing provided to order (8)
2 One put on the floor by such a tackle? (5)
3 Deserve to muddle one labouring in the dock (9)
4 Excited by a function held by staff (7)
5 Arrive earlier, parking on slope backwards (7)
6 Grab a silver piece for boy (5)
7 Second-best individual accepting a role as emperor (9)
8 Old policeman useful in the kitchen (6)
14 One taking part in fight with the monarch's side? (9)
15 Poet endlessly interrupting the blighter, another poet (9)
16 Fish thrashing about – it's angry (8)
18 A worm, husband behaving despicably (7)
19 Most of Taurus included in local type of star cluster (7)
20 Middling warm? Severe heat (6)
22 Girl with love that could make cowboy a good catch? (5)
24 Take aim in uniform (5)

ACROSS

1 Some of a brick structure (6)
5 A beautiful creature about to supply drink (8)
10 Turned mushrooms into a more-or-less risky investment (4)
11 Stay calm and endure punishment, Midshipman (4,2,4)
12 Gun's part is to blast gap in fortifications, we hear (6)
13 Beauty treatment's price due to be altered (8)
14 Contribute to act (4,1,4)
18 Chinese philosophical principle used in, for example, contemplation (5)
19 Authorised to go with expedition (5)
20 Prudence given help in training (9)
24 Recurrent suspicion about blooming programme (8)
25 One wantonly damaging museum finally left (6)
26 Colin acted badly in Western (10)
27 Daughter put in son's form (4)
28 Female turned and spoke haltingly (8)
29 Tax put on author's literary output (6)

DOWN

2 In dismay, note what goes on (7)
3 Boisterous and batty? (7)
4 In dressing, you have to draw level (7)
6 Front person – the one ruling now (9)
7 Inordinately raise rent and legal fees (9)
8 Running down upstart caught in traffic (9)
9 Fighter making escape with boat (9)
14 European right to finish quickly (6,3)
15 Like Disraeli's side, shifting allegiance endlessly (9)
16 A way to put on too much rouge going from side to side (9)
17 Wealth can supply a barrier to contain infection (9)
21 Cover up card player having accepted Bulgarian cash (7)
22 Base in which I belong has moved (7)
23 Squirrel more strenuous when love is involved (7)

15

ACROSS

1   Beat using stick (5)
4   Low accommodation, in a fashion, with little room (9)
9   This Johnny could show more éclat (9)
10 Quartz found in a mountain pass (5)
11 Movable feasts for elderly waiters (5,2,6)
14 August follower of Irish clan (4)
15 Belonging to second joint on leg, for example (10)
18 Cook's fat, and getting more dumpy (10)
19 Drug addict's employer (4)
21 Jumbo set aside – it's viciously difficult! (5,8)
24 Drop a theatrical piece (5)
25 School places for those needing remedial treatment (9)
27 Title for Sophia – one making her cross? (9)
28 Become dejected listening to Olive, say (5)

DOWN

1   Start out to look quickly inside ancient manuscript (10)
2   Settled a way round (3)
3   Cut out drill without hesitation (6)
4   Revolutionary organisation has business manager initially put in prison (9)
5   Stagger from place where one may be left in trouble (5)
6   Broadcasts are a must for those wanting play purely for enjoyment (8)
7   Insensitivity shown when one is put out (11)
8   In Baltimore we root for the pitcher (4)
12 Fitting pocket (11)
13 Presumably it can throw light on the other side (6,4)
16 Push particular goods – they help to raise sales, we hear (9)
17 Male worker concealing name still (8)
20 Thwarted, being in a place without parking (6)
22 To succeed, English knight has to go to law (5)
23 In the sound, notices a cutter (4)
26 Scene of carnival and endless wild revelry (3)

ACROSS

1   Rodent's limb cat is about to grab (6)
5   Mob's shifting alliance (8)
9   Divided up Japanese fencing, available in natural wood colour (6,4)
10 Ride gives feeling of elation (4)
11 Thought about a second one before beginning to drink (8)
12 Final instruction for beauty's toilette once? Exactly (4,2)
13 One pound rejected in country using francs (4)
15 Gun broken, relished using bare hands (8)
18 Solemn pronouncement in betting record that could pull punters in (4-4)
19 Duke making heartless premier (4)
21 Indirect route – the way one gets into security zone? (6)
23 For project, display too many pictures? (8)
25 It stops money being offered as bribe (4)
26 The first thing to stick in anyone's throat (5,5)
27 One way and another, holding a level (8)
28 Acting head, say, going into 4's payment (6)

DOWN

2   A colour nearly used for suit (5)
3   It's expedient to create simple dress (9)
4   One's housed junior officer deprived of place in France (6)
5   Ideal place for castles in the air? (5-6-4)
6   Failure to employ lower-class pundit (3-5)
7   I reduced misery round house (5)
8   Scraps with abandoned maidens, perhaps (9)
14 She takes a lot of trouble to compose her features (5,4)
16 Where one drives to get such clothes, perhaps (3,3,3)
17 African country was to ban dancing (8)
20 One detects old magistrate's sound (6)
22 Element offering new support for old craft (5)
24 Fibre finally eaten only when cooked (5)

17

ACROSS

1 Potato salad in US? As a rule, it's depressing (7,3)
6 Boss outstanding in game of cards (4)
9 In successive notes, loving to be disparaging (10)
10 Excessive concern some of us showed (4)
12 What's expert done? (12)
15 Cause of epidemic usually cut by two-thirds (9)
17 Private's less than perfect shot (5)
18 Splendid opening of tattoo in Edinburgh, okay? (5)
19 Tourists may be shown this mistake (9)
20 Where all the world was a stage? (5,7)
24 Group of students long affected by cut (4)
25 African hell-hole home to a Scot (10)
26 Pirate shot (4)
27 Meal partly cooked with sauce (10)

DOWN

1 Moderate coverage for members in part of France (4)
2 Approximate noise of bird (4)
3 Region of England in business releases (4,8)
4 Fight round roadblock, initially (3-2)
5 Fantastic rope, in a way, that can get one off the ground (9)
7 Risky thing to do in swimming race, at the end? (5-3-2)
8 Wants ideas rated differently (10)
11 Numbers of Romans to overhaul administrative organisation (5,7)
13 Rope highly tangled – it's hard to unravel (10)
14 A heartless lie to trouble enthusiast (10)
16 The sort of craze that's never longlasting? (9)
21 Perplexed, but not high and dry (2,3)
22 Substance it's right to extract from corn before grinding (4)
23 Possible conclusions reached by trial jury could be just (4)

18

ACROSS

1   Making no progress in set problem (6)
5   Daub page in a couple of seconds (8)
9   County's season not a productive period (8)
10 Despicable type conclusively no great shakes? (6)
11 Decorate wings of priory, bringing back more appropriate interior (8)
12 Sort of tennis the Spanish watch (8)
13 Very small measure of coffee or large 'un, perhaps (7)
16 Belgian flying from part of India (7)
20 Endlessly hang about after breakdown driving here in Austria (8)
22 Sweep – cricket stroke that's straightforward (5-3)
23 Intense anger uncalled for, with seconds out (6)
24 Late news swamped by distant crisis (8)
25 Home Guard the old, old soldier trains with? (8)
26 Excited socialist given roasting (3-3)

DOWN

2   Players hoping for a full house from pack, say? (6)
3   Element found in West when in short supply (8)
4   Crooked fence, perhaps (8)
5   A High Church point of view? (7)
6   Championship point wasted following disturbance (8)
7   Two sorts of wrong topping on a pancake (8)
8   Sort of football played in school match (5,5)
12 Can drug, say, become such a sweet substance? (5,5)
14 Trusted friend to change self-image (5,3)
15 It's not usually fair for this to be put up (8)
17 Scene that has none of the actors in (8)
18 Film star bound to go to the wall (5,3)
19 Queen captured in crazy attack (7)
21 Doubled up laughing about new Conservative leader (6)

19

ACROSS

1 Barrier that doesn't affect one's prospects (2-2)
3 Perversely blame a skit apt to be taken the wrong way (10)
9 Line of soldiers humming (4)
10 Let off dwellings where solid fuel is used (10)
12 Strait-laced girl breaking into old-fashioned language (9)
13 Fancy line in pattern (5)
14 Vehicle seldom free of rattle (12)
18 Athlete keeping intellectual woman (12)
21 Coarse woman including new unconventional words (5)
22 Experience again happiness going round old city (9)
24 Feeling mere pathos, perhaps (10)
25 Car burning at centre of motorway (4)
26 Where a woman can sit after getting up (4-6)
27 Well protected, with artillery backing (4)

DOWN

1 Dance involving sailors, one form of exercise (8)
2 Not paid when old and grey, and not included (8)
4 One bowling is carrying the side – a famous spinner (5)
5 Sort of warfare soldier, say, found vigorous (9)
6 Colourful reflections produced by round trip by tube (12)
7 Vessel fatal to punters? (6)
8 Without effort, very probably (6)
11 Wordy historians? (12)
15 Discovered how circuit might be dangerous? (9)
16 Reducing strength of old unit, I become disorderly (8)
17 Correspondence about getting on outside (8)
19 Utter halfwit is kept outside tests (6)
20 Preserved – as one expects to be on the M25? (6)
23 Conservative said to be sort of pink (5)

20

ACROSS

1 Take a chance in selection, given last word for a change (4,4)
6 Wonder if poet has finally lost money (6)
9 Marketplace accepting new sort of goat (6)
10 Relax heartless command for one who returns (8)
11 Explorer's incomplete claim rejected in island (8)
12 Revolting team's taken advantage (6)
13 Seabirds see another one returning on board (5)
14 Parasite that traditionally overlooks displays of affection (9)
17 Saw covering page by writer as something extra (9)
19 Break one's skin (5)
22 False allure of poetry prize (6)
23 One heavily criticised about nothing and taken apart (8)
24 Living off the land (8)
25 Of dusky appearance? (6)
26 Woollen material from pullover initially altered (6)
27 Rehearsal of Suite in G (8)

DOWN

2 Thoroughly examine and torture a pair of partners imprisoned (7)
3 Sea creature swallows sole, swimming in huge quantities (9)
4 Old people left inside shrine (6)
5 Overnight, I slink off, being such a shy person (9,6)
6 Doctors having gone on round found carrier of disease (8)
7 Judgment made by composer about time (7)
8 Start to recognise something hereditary in girl's size (9)
13 Party activity finds growing support around shopping centre (5,4)
15 Rivalry from Greek character accepted in good mood (9)
16 Sin that subverts real duty (8)
18 Brown is after place as tradesman (7)
20 Don, perhaps, from African country lacking capital (7)
21 Barwoman's wine, excellent when brought up (6)

ACROSS

1 Return of Verdi's opera incomplete without very great singer (4)
3 Special offer with cost finally reduced? That's natural (10)
9 Depression in the land so long (4)
10 Criminal came and left in disguise (10)
12 Washerwoman needs to use soft soap, putting in cape (9)
13 Stout is to be served inside (5)
14 Seat for parlourmaid? (7,5)
18 A pedlar, so we hear, is never taking it so easy on the road (12)
21 Mocking religious leader leaving this order (5)
22 One reckons new university projection's 100 short (9)
24 Terminate old arrangement? It depends on the strings attached (10)
25 Exempt from charge to cross river (4)
26 Evidence provided that's getting rid of monarch (10)
27 Part of cathedral, say – such as Ely? (4)

DOWN

1 Swoop down on honky-tonk with a lot of money (4-4)
2 Changing a lot, and not particularly nice about it? (8)
4 Money is stolen from a saint (5)
5 Toss up on part of square (9)
6 Way to deal with sin etc. (12)
7 Detective has to have permit for peephole (6)
8 One whose charges are small for easy task (6)
11 IOUs, possibly, for such gems? (4-8)
15 Open spaces standard for martial art (5,4)
16 Birds from the freezing poles (8)
17 A piece of armour said to inflict injury (8)
19 Blurred shot (6)
20 Finish off sauce on prawn cocktail – cover all over (6)
23 Transport system Parisians look down on? (5)

ACROSS

1 Hold in subjection in dungeon below (4,5)
6 Joins course (5)
9 Inhuman as Capek's workers were (7)
10 It's used for washing city, however backward (7)
11 Leaders in Arabia blame Yankee soldiers meddling in the Gulf (5)
12 Weather-beaten players were in tears (9)
13 Artist I encountered in Montana (5)
14 Separation of one run of three notes in advance (9)
17 Last month I got married, being weakened (9)
18 Fish that's seen between two rays (5)
19 Brave measure rejected in reform (9)
22 Visitor is supposed to speak (5)
24 Proclaim harlot's execution (7)
25 Line is a little flexible (7)
26 A number sleep before noon or practise meditation? (5)
27 Gambling activity in horse-racing centre (9)

DOWN

1 Destiny of religious leader protected by god of love (5)
2 Rudimentary mistakes by incomer (9)
3 Terms finally stated – from last month I'm linked with a corporation (9)
4 Two indict knight with corruption – and mayor (4,11)
5 Mischievous spirit or goblin of old we recollected (5,10)
6 Lily takes Abraham's nephew to the States (5)
7 In preservation, it remains of some use (5)
8 Junior officer has position and wealth (9)
13 Damaged – up to a point, 17 given treatment (9)
15 Insensitivity to pain seen from different angle in the East (9)
16 Warm spot in valley leading to old pass (9)
20 Sailor knocking out leader of the police in excitement (5)
21 Plant rising among short heather (5)
23 Lifting? It takes time to hoist (5)

ACROSS

1 Hence Jumbo may bring many excitement? Hard to disagree! (8)
5 Power increased by river's flow (6)
10 In which statesmen take advantage of passing the buck? (6,9)
11 More spruce getting a sprinkling of nitrate (7)
12 A city with no land set apart (7)
13 Ordered to admit composer leaving a European capital (8)
15 No use going by smell of decomposing matter (5)
18 Busy step, with a movement to the front (5)
20 Fine work of art is attractive (8)
23 Elect to enter river in the buff (7)
25 Get firm to give leave to boy (7)
26 Account I managed to turn into plenty (3-3-4-5)
27 One of Lawrence's seven wise supporters (6)
28 Old college has gone off having several unions (8)

DOWN

1 Not revealing the punishment (6)
2 Plot to immerse me in the entire Bible? (9)
3 Going for the title (7)
4 Getting on reclaimed land, dislodging the top (5)
6 Affect to have received honour? That's intolerable (3,4)
7 Animal found in East German region (5)
8 County papers clearing first page for council leader (8)
9 Such an heir father brought up – mother, too, perhaps (8)
14 King of Wessex's firm, banishing daughter without roof over head (8)
16 Maiden in Nebraska overcoming barrier to become brave's wife (9)
17 Disadvantage of useful-sounding EC policy (8)
19 Run out and move round building (7)
21 Keen to go round a part of Europe (7)
22 Sinuously attractive, but extremely shy about relationship (6)
24 Lively claret at last available in small bottle (5)
25 Little sketch of fawn left out nothing (5)

ACROSS

1   Jump on horse and get going (5,2)
5   Amounts expressed numerically as squares, say (7)
9   Senior officer likely to appear heartless in most cases (9)
10 Bend in river in neat part of London (5)
11 American imprisoned by Lincoln for insulting language (5)
12 Not even one of the Baker Street boys, for example (9)
13 Oppose the production of chickens – a very shady activity (5-8)
17 Looking at other people's hands, one knows what's on the cards (7-6)
21 Obscene publication's original plan (9)
24 Drastically affect with revolting object (5)
25 Contemplating year one had in England (5)
26 Tom Jones, for one, came across the heath (9)
27 One working to make dough sounds like poor person (7)
28 Without a clue, don't enter so much data (7)

DOWN

1   Striking gesture (6)
2   One who may appear in a flash (9)
3   Fuss about river exercise creating danger to shipping (7)
4   Sounds like affectionate donkey's given bedding (9)
5   Entrance hall designed to meet needs of the old within (5)
6   So-called farmer briefly in charge of agricultural work (7)
7   Take to the streets and dance around Bull's Head (5)
8   Wise man keeping jug for removal of water (8)
14 Game player in a loose scrum is dumbfounded (9)
15 Realise it is wrong for this old citizen (9)
16 It's delivered by hand to striker not working with the rest (3-5)
18 Such work lacks order and is not called for (7)
19 Article attached to line, wet, here? (7)
20 A Degas reproduction more than one saw (6)
22 Marry single sweetheart (5)
23 Gather inside train ferry (5)

ACROSS

1 In cattle, find English favouring this breed? (8)
5 Snigger from thief (6)
8 Having broken heart, peaceful type was idling (6,4)
9 Genuine-sounding folk music (4)
10 Hold flexible opinions – as banditti do? (4,2,4,4)
11 They may illuminate pit orchestra's section (7)
13 Taking over from Tom, the sailor (7)
15 Polished poem turned into opera (7)
18 Litter – offensive plague (7)
21 Keenness of operators to make theatre cleaner (8,6)
22 Sacred river comes from mountain height (4)
23 American form of transport extended by city in Alabama (10)
24 Be visibly embarrassed giving court order to diplomat (6)
25 In an ugly spill, being clumsy (8)

DOWN

1 Bowler, say, beginning to control the wayward cutter (7)
2 Much loved commander captured, got back (9)
3 Type of bond for builder injuring himself (7)
4 In working hours, doctor supplies lozenge (7)
5 Extreme position of a prime minister – Paderewski, for example (5,4)
6 Don't allow to finish dog-end (7)
7 Nature writer upsets me – fellow's not quiet (7)
12 Remove bird tucking into flower (9)
14 Popular translation putting things back to front (9)
16 Manlike? Not according to Donne (7)
17 Within this range, we hear (7)
18 Aircraft that's blown up (7)
19 Go down to see graduate's record of academic achievement (7)
20 Extremely lucky as fur-trapper – it's a chancy business (7)

ACROSS

1   Sweet nonsense (6)
5   Surrealist's courage in grip of defeat (8)
9   Domineering type damaged cart with another vehicle (8)
10 Compensation welcomed by those who hate TV? (6)
11 Wood, bound with wire, apt to be made ready (8)
12 An officer with bearing of a star (6)
13 English platoon leader redistributed rations (8)
15 Return first-class to one continent or another (4)
17 Undemanding section of *Sea Symphony* (4)
19 Butterflies in girl's hair, perhaps (8)
20 Note indiscretion and pass by (6)
21 Peacemakers tense, we hear? That's natural (8)
22 Sect to reform into musical groups (6)
23 Concerned with what's tabled in parliament, call back (8)
24 Sat with Sun, perhaps, keeping to routine (3-2-3)
25 Dealer in military supplies said to be more cunning (6)

DOWN

2   Wails, having to lay a remarkable specimen up (8)
3   Black barrier surrounding our new row (8)
4   Frenchman's merry, eating coarse biscuit (9)
5   Composed astounding rhyme for mid-Lent time (9,6)
6   Gentlemanly thief's ways to redistribute wealth (7)
7   Devil's habitat down under (8)
8   Flag in Tyne flying for unity (8)
14 Celebrity in sergeants' mess (9)
15 Radio set adjusted for a space traveller (8)
16 Young child given small railway and soldiers (8)
17 Starters in eatery soon chewed up, followed by fast food (8)
18 So great, to admire people of similar kind (8)
19 Rice dish to stir in stew, adding tabasco finally? (7)

ACROSS

1 Spending less on party, and reducing effort (6-6)
9 Jacket worn by Emma or Rebecca, say (4,5)
10 Wife embracing a husband returning to Eastern state (5)
11 One of the first books going out (6)
12 Start play after tough's dismissed (5,3)
13 Fashion team is into such rich fabric (6)
15 Lamb, for example, in casseroles, say, is tasty (8)
18 It's enough to keep the corporation occupied (8)
19 Carry out surgical operation for pain (6)
21 Resigned after editor's move to change layout (8)
23 Going the wrong way, falls again to spinner (6)
26 Withdraw from a foreign state (5)
27 Destruction of fox in Kent one immediately related (4,2,3)
28 Whistler's inspiration? A source of light (8,4)

DOWN

1 These go up where many snakes go down (7)
2 One who sings old catch, to begin with (5)
3 Riding on noble railway into the interior (9)
4 Prevent score to avoid losing (4)
5 Raised one card-player endlessly, with king and four aces (8)
6 Coward holding end of bomb for explosives expert (5)
7 Speculator – one who believes gold must be retained (8)
8 A good chairperson covers it (6)
14 Singer that's old-fashioned in changing times (8)
16 In favour of authentic choral music (9)
17 Writer opening up, invaded by press (8)
18 Poet's craft manifested in elaborate style, none the less (6)
20 Rook and duck included by king, in place of other birds (7)
22 Cunning exercise producing passage needed for chapter (5)
24 Agreed, after rising, to accept king's view (5)
25 Beheaded old German – some nerve! (4)

ACROSS

1 Bird's perch, perhaps, set between rulers (10)
6 Moor was killed – that's terrible (4)
9 Unable to afford passage, serve amidships in ungodly surroundings (10)
10 So gang leader abandons gangsters (4)
12 Part of shoe that meant the world to Hans Sachs? (4)
13 Literary family member appears to love new suit (3,4,2)
15 Expected to fall early in competition, not having been drilled (8)
16 Flinch from requirement for wedding in church (6)
18 Academic stream strive endlessly to get university place (6)
20 Tornado, perhaps, seen to twist one way (8)
23 Stop people going to hell (9)
24 March girl across river in military group (4)
26 Superior rejected Derby, say, for religious settlement (4)
27 Ceremonial officer became rare after reorganisation (4-6)
28 Demolish an oriental paradox (4)
29 Breaking down on tenth lap in athletics competition (10)

DOWN

1 In danger, king raised dagger (4)
2 Writer sent up hacks, as boys related (7)
3 Option that may spoil a hitherto clear round (5,7)
4 Maid has unsettled rest, tucking in legs (8)
5 Justice is in investors' interest (6)
7 Level of responsibility staggered fighting units (7)
8 City fails to pull in financial supporter (3,7)
11 No one can come in to land, say, ahead of him (4,8)
14 Concussed wife-beater taken down (5-5)
17 Happily try, but extremely dim (8)
19 As a doctor, order to take up port (7)
21 Dim potential in land-locked sea for him? (7)
22 Six against one – that's sounding lively (6)
25 Ibsen's play mostly indigestible stuff (4)

ACROSS

1 At first sight demure, one gets caught in a grimace (5,5)
7 Found actors making an appearance (4)
9 Coins are unusual in outline (8)
10 Cut one piece of material to go round front of nightdress (6)
11 The purpose of camping (6)
12 Gift tied up at work (8)
13 Disposition to get sentence reversed (4)
15 It could spatter oil about me (10)
18 Stopped taking bets? It's incomprehensible (6,4)
20 From active vent, molten lava finally seen here (4)
21 Prize gold before iron when it comes to posh French dish (3-2-3)
24 Drink (hot) available in water bottle (6)
26 Turned a novel event into an opera (6)
27 Journey by road or air transport (8)
28 Quote a lot of speech (4)
29 Progressive advantage involved capturing rook (5-5)

DOWN

2 Music produced by fabulous bird right inside hill (4,1,4)
3 Whale swallowing krill, primarily, in abundant supply (5)
4 Direct leading seaman (5-4)
5 In uneven position hold game up – it can take the heat off (7)
6 Order English dictionary (5)
7 Possibly a special artist (9)
8 Scrap with ringleader in cast (5)
14 In court, is standard completely different? (9)
16 Force group of workers to become temporary (9)
17 Sleepy place fratricide fled to (4,2,3)
19 Sprayed it upon a cactus (7)
22 Some inferior ibices and antelope (5)
23 Plants left in public squares (5)
25 Prize given to a resort in the Mediterranean (5)

ACROSS

1   Dreadfully offend a tar everywhere on board (4,3,3)
6   Outside parts of cake I had covered thus? (4)
9   Said whether I could provide meteorological expertise (7,3)
10 Poor-quality houses endlessly collapse (4)
12 Portraying eccentrics, some of Carroll's characters (7,5)
15 Beat up? (9)
17 Gather fine ordered by king (5)
18 Temporary accommodation hard to find after nine (5)
19 Instruct drunk about English drinks (9)
20 Where all the world was a stage? (5,7)
24 Almost dark, but not quite (4)
25 Engine crewmen gently brush (4-6)
26 One gets stuck in bottleneck here in Ireland (4)
27 Indulging in horseplay with the blue poet? Good! (10)

DOWN

1   Show great affection for young animal (4)
2   Interpret article in Russian (4)
3   Old hero's sole weakness? Yes and no (8,4)
4   At meeting, American might tip this for the big race (5)
5   Going to fire from this vessel? That's even more dangerous (6-3)
7   Church left room for varying number (10)
8   Flower mother, on request, got out of bed (6,4)
11 One must be behind the lines before action can start (12)
13 Apt to be shot? (10)
14 Tradesman rearranging morning round with hesitation (10)
16 As director, prepare to shoot after hold-up (9)
21 She's here today, gone tomorrow (5)
22 Scandinavian destroyer left Fair Isle (4)
23 Composer looked up to in Africa (4)

ACROSS

1 European partner, so-called (5)
4 Reviewing amount of money the china raised (7-2)
9 For which a lifeline is essential at the seaside (9)
10 Cancel membership fees, being out of credit (5)
11 Doctor cured sweetheart – needed to lose weight (6)
12 Very willing to shorten one of these flowers? (8)
14 Grotesque giant (9)
16 Left with king at end of game, it can help one draw (5)
17 One acts on impulse, showing courage (5)
19 Dregs the Spanish birds eat (9)
21 Use it to get capital, vital after move (5,3)
22 Fairy's bound to come first for liveliness (6)
25 Attack from the kickoff (5)
26 Unknown coin got in change (9)
27 Sweetheart as loving as a TV character (9)
28 Chatters loudly about North Americans (5)

DOWN

1 Intended, say, to leave husband outside the emporium (10,5)
2 Drawn out of line, like the walls in mah-jong? (5)
3 Shock treatment for a page-boy, perhaps (7)
4 Composer, not one to overindulge (4)
5 Flower, maybe, lost some pieces finally falling off (3,7)
6 One privy to secrets imprisoned by king (7)
7 Church high-ups spouting from the gutter! (9)
8 Books about religious education heartily deplore the making of images (6,9)
13 Language bound to make one too embarrassed to speak (6-4)
15 Self-regarding youth Russians caught misbehaving (9)
18 Allow mistake to nettle one (7)
20 In no state to accept, for example, a bunch of flowers (7)
23 Rule not all dare ignore (5)
24 Muffler endlessly wound (4)

ACROSS

1 A bit of excitement about a travelling fair and animal show (6,4)
6 On one's own, so going back into city (4)
9 Like insects, say (10)
10 Either part of pontoon bridge, for example (4)
12 Fatal direction recommended to young man (4)
13 Begin to make deletions (6,3)
15 Distance moved in travel (8)
16 Author who adds fuel to the flames? (6)
18 Take off comic finally in highly unpopular comeback (6)
20 Quiet performance in theatre of French doctors with method (4,4)
23 Eddy's stimulating sort of bath (9)
24 Freight lacking at first for old ship (4)
26 March price rise (4)
27 Spanish city full of bad fruit (10)
28 Look equal (4)
29 Badly frightened boy is held by mistake (10)

DOWN

1 Rule, for example, about 12 (4)
2 Female to certify as being extremely fertile (7)
3 Quake circles earth, as this shows (7,5)
4 Measures taken by sailor as aid to navigation (4,4)
5 Get heated and make sharp reply (6)
7 Silver, for example, main explorer found (3-4)
8 Result of poor return, perhaps? Name ruined (10)
11 He stands on a progressive platform (12)
14 Don't buy anything from double-glazing seller? (6-4)
17 Name ship after European capitalist? (8)
19 Slow rate of progress for such a charger (7)
21 Ugly woman with bad legs seeks best offer (7)
22 In spring, sweet companion goes to church (6)
25 Bundle of notes includes new spelling aid (4)

33

ACROSS

1 Make waves, as rough sea may (4,3,4)
7 Set a limit to EC policy (3)
9 Relative's put on almost two flipping stone (9)
10 Turkish leader elected for second term (5)
11 Wrestle with complications, and become heated (7)
12 Patent medicine is in no way unusual (7)
13 Brilliant solver of clues used by Telegraph (5)
15 As a consequence of backing murderer, doctor's unable to sleep (9)
17 Half of our capital allocated to country house, with an eye to the future (4-5)
19 Said to constrict Prometheus, for one (5)
20 Dishes used to start the set (7)
22 Teacher's first reprimand can make you sad (7)
24 Black eye doctor has to treat (5)
25 Don't put on rouge, say? It's detestable (4,5)
27 Sign agreement fellow backed (3)
28 Dominate game many go to see in London (5,6)

DOWN

1 They observed an enormous bird (3)
2 Scoundrels start to employ bad language (5)
3 One acting legally for another, as set out in actual case (7)
4 Trip over cross dog raised commotion (9)
5 Once at sea, crossing a body of water (5)
6 Beam at stern matrons misbehaving (7)
7 Facility at ski resort for the upwardly mobile (9)
8 Main link opened by US in 1914 (6,5)
11 After herbal remedies, I am taking dope (6,5)
14 Organise deliveries in deceitful practice (3-6)
16 With relocation, protects a witness (9)
18 Try wearing torn clothing (7)
19 Flight simulator – it helps you run (7)
21 Push to one side distress over having gained weight (5)
23 No end of chicken in China cooked like this? (5)
26 Watch or clock I heard (3)

ACROSS

1   Its majority shareholder gets a desirable opportunity (8)
5   Ominously appear, in good year, to become depressed (6)
8   A sandwich? Hardly! (6,4)
9   Box, for example, that's made of wood (4)
10   But for friend, I'd get involved in illicit pleasure (9,5)
11   Supply the flower-girl outside (7)
13   Work out how to maintain attack (4,3)
15   Himalayan creature less deadly when beheaded? (3-4)
18   Scrap with chaps in extra time (7)
21   Former PM blunt where military exercises are involved (9,5)
22   Fuel used in older vehicles (4)
23   Orchid sharing 10 in the garden (4-3-3)
24   Discover where bad man's hiding in this country (6)
25   Not good enough to be Secretary-general, perhaps (8)

DOWN

1   Sadly reflecting on university learner's swift breakdown (7)
2   She acts as a maid, often (9)
3   Where people queue for drinks between pieces of music? (3,4)
4   Fix wedding for 17th of March, say (4,3)
5   Good early composer, the source of much that is precious (9)
6   Bound to excel (7)
7   Characters in trams, i.e. conductors (7)
12   One can take far too much interest in his business (4,5)
14   Female teenager contrived to become independent operator (4,5)
16   Did visit someone over the hill (3-4)
17   British girl in foreign country (7)
18   Bow, perhaps, as king enters, in sultanate (7)
19   Cursorily study horse I'd mounted initially (3,4)
20   Girl, during plague, hides here for treatment (7)

ACROSS

1   Capital source of milk for doctor? (6)
5   No book-lover, but he's not common (8)
9   David shows MP is last resort (8)
10 Raise a bit of money before the match (4,2)
11 Having left path, I will return to Welsh town (8)
12 Guard required for prince's cortege (6)
13 Display, we hear, horse or cow (8)
15 Quails when the governor appears around five (4)
17 Put one's foot in it? On the contrary, hand (4)
19 Celebration of life as TV broadcast (8)
20 Exhausting task making king more poorly (6)
21 Boys meeting in part of France (8)
22 Get behind duck on body of water (6)
23 Pictures of mature insects (8)
24 Flier's performance in air? (8)
25 Continue without a glance backwards (4,2)

DOWN

2   Discarded fish has to be thrown outside (8)
3   Island state with military officer on top (8)
4   Unlike the small print, it's very obvious (4,5)
5   Against being a candidate as yet (15)
6   Appear to understand brief examination (4,3)
7   Feel nostalgic for our island state (8)
8   He shows favouritism where set point is involved (8)
14 Current director puts one part of speech in order (5-4)
15 Reserve card for service to readers (4,4)
16 No citizen could be more unpleasant about convict (8)
17 Take part in pilot activity to test public opinion (3,1,4)
18 Diagnose incorrectly in US city (3,5)
19 Old kings speaking for island group (7)

ACROSS

1 Contemporary dependent on those of little stature (2-2-3-6)
8 One gets benefit, though not old or unemployed (4)
9 Erect? Just the opposite, by the sound of it (5)
10 Team expressed unrestrained glee (4)
11 Player given terrible roasting (8)
12 Reliable, though at first impaired by neglect (6)
13 Grey place in the Yukon (10)
16 Ignoring the odds, Olga and Linda bet (4)
17 Labour organisation's turned tail (4)
18 Has replied in order to get post as a salesman (10)
20 Shrub of specified sort mother put in (6)
22 Insertion of a word like this by no means straightforward? (8)
24 The way I run a prison (4)
25 Flatter, truncated type of hill in America (5)
26 Some superb rigging in this vessel (4)
27 Electromotor worked without new zapper (6,7)

DOWN

1 Where the rudder is, not out in the open (5,3,7)
2 Greek character joining the volunteers (5)
3 The drains must be fixed, being befouled (9)
4 He turns out as, ultimately, the winner (7)
5 Out of place in record time (5)
6 Releases two articles in French about successful action (9)
7 This account is what shocks the beak (11,4)
14 Four-letter word from Peggy, upset about temperature (9)
15 There's always a place for putting a box, for example (9)
19 Pastiche not hard to rewrite as suitable for theatre (7)
21 Jack wearing belt as customary attire (5)
23 Composer using computer link with hesitation (5)

37

ACROSS

1 Casual way to feed tame bird? (7)
5 Renovate coat by mistake (7)
9 Like dreadfully ugly things, less good? (9)
10 Provide bachelor with token of love (5)
11 Resemble, in parts (5)
12 Lawyer is pursuing right to be in trade (9)
13 Fare on vehicle specially fixed for the elderly? (5,2,6)
17 Lines for the Fool, in production of Lear? (8,5)
21 Exercise – it's repeated in a nasty fog (3,6)
24 Crockery one piece short? It's not serious (5)
25 Musician Doolittle got news from? (5)
26 Stone originally fell near one (9)
27 Return of disease in fruit-tree I cut back (7)
28 One exhausting feature of kitchen (7)

DOWN

1 Light-hearted, though initially deprived of sight (6)
2 St. Peter's edict covering woman (9)
3 American city's impressive area (7)
4 Computer-controlled stores of fruit, about a half of basket (9)
5 In favour of keeping the old hall (5)
6 Books I hurry round to criticise (7)
7 Wordsworth's boy, one I introduced to his sister briefly (5)
8 Sort of block substantial pay increase (4-4)
14 Edward infested? Don't worry (5,4)
15 Joy about even 50% getting promotion (9)
16 Final set of questions – one's stuck, quite blank (8)
18 I fall in vain pursuit (3-4)
19 Liqueur or rum at a fair (7)
20 Dog running wild in street (6)
22 Pointless court case is to cause scandal (5)
23 They take position, accepting sheriff's lead (5)

ACROSS

1 Beetle comes to have a lasting effect on Jack (6)
5 Spectator's a weekly paper (8)
9 Police astride horses appearing promptly (4-4)
10 Old instrument in band without tuning peg (6)
11 Don't believe Duke is noble (8)
12 Swede, say, about to join golf club shortly (8)
13 University, with new advertisements, removes cause of stoppage (7)
16 Champion gets youngster into trouble (7)
20 Frank's girl nearly packed after first sign of trouble (8)
22 Elope with my excited sweetheart, one under firm control (8)
23 Fudge that's used in American biscuit (6)
24 Fruit useless for a pudding (4,4)
25 Soft and gentle as a woolly jumper (8)
26 Ravel's complicated mass (6)

DOWN

2 Though possibly heroic, he can't succeed on his own (6)
3 Intervening between sides, aspire to wipe out this? (8)
4 Working well, obliged to take place at the top (8)
5 Workman cut by smug townsman (7)
6 Unusual end of landscape by Constable, say (8)
7 Leaders given protection under covered wagon (8)
8 Like a crop system requiring total rain and nothing artificial (10)
12 Censor depressed writer (4-6)
14 Only mineral water served in this interrogation cell? (4,4)
15 Peacemakers' party outside normal working hours (8)
17 Water under the bridge? Quite the opposite (8)
18 Somerset author's agent in colourless study (8)
19 High Church feature (7)
21 Beneficial because fully content (6)

ACROSS

1 Optical instrument to get by shaping steel initially (9)
6 Pierce log (5)
9 Tees, say, daughter got from golf club (5)
10 A daily cuff that keeps the pages in order (5-4)
11 Makes shorts less neat (7)
12 Old artistic work carrying little weight in all-enveloping organisation (7)
13 Met people here, having come through Victoria, say (7,7)
17 Form studies many indications of debt, aware of social divisions (5-9)
21 Plant providing neat cutting (7)
23 Artist has no right to sound surprised (7)
25 Study one coming out of audition to find singer (9)
26 What some rotten nuisance can produce? (5)
27 Use as an excuse in parking van (5)
28 See how the land lies and start shop-lifting (4,5)

DOWN

1 Refuse to go off drink (4,4)
2 Uniform required in plane (5)
3 Hurriedly writes scores (9)
4 One who is against work has a problem (7)
5 Old story line about one of Brigadier Gerard's feats (7)
6 Bird cry with one note too high (5)
7 Hope to let out special sort of lens (9)
8 Drunken parties one leaves to get food (6)
14 A new local arrangement for a grant (9)
15 Animal raised on cattle ship in a nasty state (9)
16 Star has set out in a venture (8)
18 Policeman joining one group – he helps to direct bus (7)
19 Changed house in foreign city (3,4)
20 Having headdress with diamonds on top of the world? (3-3)
22 Liberal university Marxist found was attractive (5)
24 Love piquancy introduced to dance (5)

ACROSS

1 Move into different shares as socialist tax is introduced (12)
8 Before going after gold, saint is ascetic (7)
9 Unfortunate circumstances changed his plans around (7)
11 Small ruler used in making letters (7)
12 A lot of rupees worker collected for a year's work (7)
13 Pipe up, as one starting the day (5)
14 Batsman's aggressive plan causing unaccountable harm (3-3-3)
16 Present put in awkward position (2,3,4)
19 During Lent, for example, start to envisage this? (5)
21 The most black risks at end of gambit – king stuck in middle (7)
23 There's nothing to restrict the view (7)
24 Island gathering? (7)
25 Stress in musical group is returning (7)
26 Challenge whether goose is cooked (3,4,5)

DOWN

1 Feels bad about taking penny off offerings (7)
2 For one, matter may involve end of life (7)
3 Change round seat, dreadfully hot in awful factory (9)
4 Cuban measure of alcohol upset sailor (5)
5 He provides the band for union celebration (4,3)
6 One imparting knowledge of rough terrain (7)
7 A way to pay for certain things with regularity (7,5)
10 Support a big weight, an individual best (6,2,4)
15 Measured response from military stronghold at flier going over (3,3,3)
17 Finished with husband in depression (7)
18 Time of day when tea, say, is unavailable during horse trials (7)
19 Criminal seizes excellent porcelain (7)
20 Very silly group of ladies dancing as I come over (7)
22 About noon, cat runs off into shade (5)

41

ACROSS

1 Become smoother (7)
5 Haddock initially being mistaken for another fish (7)
9 Straightened out West Indian student in trouble (9)
10 Offer excuse for holding party in capital (5)
11 The ultimate giveaway, to absolutely no purpose (3,3,7)
13 Is it common for a painting to be so labelled? (8)
15 Plant material from river Dickensian heroine brought back (6)
17 Make sick with mouldy leftover (6)
19 Support a revolutionary in pain (8)
22 Cite religious work in speech by way of embellishment (13)
25 Pulled out, being fatigued (5)
26 Perfect excellence admirer and I share (4,5)
27 Old king is totally destructive about me (7)
28 Fiendish protest devil cut short (7)

DOWN

1 Unpleasant bird noise (4)
2 Engage in a race around short course (7)
3 Shortly it is going to become woven fabric (5)
4 Restricted relationship with boy (8)
5 Covering up corporal punishment (6)
6 Cooked rook parts for Sunday dinner (5,4)
7 Early? First of all is never in time, is always late! (7)
8 Succumbing, turn in weapon to the German (5,5)
12 Too rude for conversion, not acceptable (3,2,5)
14 Orientals in temporary homes found alternative accommodation (9)
16 Stately dance of Bedouin, say, in part of desert (8)
18 Enthusiast getting prize for tree (3,4)
20 Business at one time in credit needs new start (7)
21 Deity bringing a point to lives (6)
23 Language of people I had encountered on island (5)
24 Stoppage said to be result of political alliance (4)

ACROSS

1 Formal coat is dull at back (6)
5 Very warm longs? Exactly the opposite! (3,5)
10 Mix in jug (4)
11 Gentle light that helps restore calm mood? (4,6)
12 Casually survey sound indicators of intellectual level? (6)
13 Real mess as husband is involved in motorway accident (8)
14 Is in charge of cutting early lead (4,5)
18 Lay to rest some uncertain terror (5)
19 About to take strike – successive poor scores unthinkable (5)
20 In school, always keep working (9)
24 On appeal, reverse obvious run out (8)
25 Stroke of the pen reducing gossip by 50% (6)
26 After a deception, people divorce (10)
27 Curry leaving five-piece band one short (4)
28 Love-poetry about affair too much of a good thing? (8)
29 Get a mouthful, having forty winks in church (6)

DOWN

2 Goddess with a heavenly body, note (7)
3 Went straight, although wearing old convict gear? (7)
4 Son received into respectable family line (7)
6 Tradesman ready to sell more likely to survive? (9)
7 Puppet on string should get laugh at last (9)
8 City – no need to move here from mine? (9)
9 Extra on bill, to take tea in rush (9)
14 Tricky situation for consumer liable to get fingers burnt? (3,6)
15 Leisurely outings to fish in Lake District area (9)
16 Cut the drones out (9)
17 Fit American carrying soldier's equipment (9)
21 This sort of act a sin (7)
22 Tax bill up in surrounding city-state (7)
23 Fillet to go round untidy hair (7)

43

ACROSS

1 It may be Venetian marble, but that's as far as one can go (5,5)
6 Little woman in punt with husband (4)
10 Central section of wardrobe seeming heavy (5)
11 Very hot ordinary seaman in waders (9)
12 Improvised fashion garment (9)
13 Sea receding round very immature creature (5)
14 Give ground for a sanctuary (7)
15 Sugary sweetheart embraced by Frank (7)
17 Flourish from bugler at the front to give encouragement (7)
19 Contemptible people belonging to separate schools (7)
21 Turn to celebrate prize in America (5)
23 Thanks to this section, the Emperor came to life (9)
24 Metal bat Australian opener's seen breaking (9)
25 Defective retina almost unresponsive (5)
26 Teller's ability to detect those voting against (4)
27 Forebear reporting outrageously about love (10)

DOWN

1 Amelia's slip (7)
2 Create ski specially for winter sports person (3-6)
3 Practice progressively unnecessary for strippers (5,9)
4 As socialist, departed before one's time (7)
5 Flexible people ultimately remain in charge (7)
7 Enthusiastic wave to audience (5)
8 Darby, for example, has to manage thriftily (7)
9 Place that sells juice satisfying Victoria, for one (7,7)
16 Elected successor of Winston could be merciless (9)
17 One of Peel's hounds involved in perilous hunt (7)
18 New university getting free kind of energy (7)
19 Cold-blooded type with hidden depths (7)
20 Legislator involved in treason (7)
22 Rendezvous with beautiful woman finally changed (5)

44

ACROSS

1 A container that's not properly shut (4)
3 Reverse of jolly character (4)
6 Pink belt (5)
10 Yellowish-brown dirt covering lead (7)
11 Contract made by South and North, unexpectedly overcoming East (7)
12 Take Metro with dean, perhaps, to see this cathedral (5,4)
13 Tender put out to sea from *Queen Elizabeth* (5)
14 Soundly crush nut (6)
16 American singer having miserable time (8)
18 Come across and record deliveries (8)
19 Businessman is very convincing (6)
22 In church, has to do some engraving (5)
23 Sport seen in equestrian venue (9)
25 Paddy swears by it (7)
26 Drinks English and Chinese medicine (7)
27 Catches salmon that's been preserved, say (5)
28 Vessel at Land's End, in what condition? (4)
29 I must quit academic post to become a cleaner (4)

DOWN

1 Handbook shows a piece coated with resin (7)
2 Savings account written up as something worth having (5)
4 Dreadful experience of French exam is overwhelming (6)
5 Males try desperately to appear so! (8)
6 To be a greengrocer, one must have expertise (4,4,6)
7 Reserve troops are not dressed (3,2,4)
8 Socialist supporting friendly relations (7)
9 A part of geese I'd processed? (4,2,4,4)
15 Looking back regretfully at closing variety (9)
17 Coastline seen from quarters on ship (8)
18 Noise level of CD i.e. adjusted to be loud, initially (7)
20 Beat time right for American singer (7)
21 Commercial money-changing is slow (6)
24 Committee that needs real power like this (5)

ACROSS

1   Fabric to make daughter a cloak (6)
4   On the inside of vessel smear processed cheese (8)
10 Old crawler used to get around the King (7)
11 Bore showing some strength of character (7)
12 I get pistol out, creating a flap (10)
13 It sounds as if quay makes this charge (4)
15 It's not *batter* one finds in jug (7)
17 After drink it's right to have unruly youth warned (7)
19 Extremist moving out from the centre to trap Conservative (7)
21 Falling around river, like heavy rain (7)
23 Bear originally towards a large island (4)
24 Details of contract making little impression (5,5)
27 Tool was first immersed in acid (7)
28 Unusual place is indeed unusual! (7)
29 Acquiescent, i.e. effective with response (8)
30 Messenger carried by another messenger (6)

DOWN

1   Artistic technique that could give boxer a problem (9)
2   In the market-place, Times is propounding one socio-economic theory (7)
3   Second nasty situation, something hairy bringing nervous breakdown (5-5)
5   Name of chief, one lacking adornment (9)
6   Harbour a spy (4)
7   Academic discipline that may or may not have an object (7)
8   Born with penny once – then why, say, penniless? (5)
9   Moving third to first in exam? Revoke the change (4)
14 Maybe half the earth is covered by plant in this place (10)
16 A good person to consider, for example (4,5)
18 Drug jab – the thing a learner is after (9)
20 Young socialite can take a hint – no upper-class disaster (7)
22 I had one cast in one unusual metal (7)
23 Cold having got out of bed, dad makes hot drink (5)
25 Record tip (4)
26 Appeal when happiness is unsure? (4)

ACROSS

1 Great pains taken with this old hand-press (10)
7 Part of the arm of the law for Collins? (4)
9 Soldiers parachuting – a bit of a shower! (8)
10 Relax stern attitude about period of austerity (6)
11 Like a seabird following ship (6)
12 Found mean way to claim antique (8)
13 Condemn monk to eat nothing (4)
15 Clones are, anyway (3,3,4)
18 One late with the rent? Law having no effect (4,6)
20 At first, don't bother to lower wall (4)
21 Good speaker rejected material outside grasp (8)
24 Arduous peaks, Everest included (6)
26 Better propeller for boat (6)
27 One deserting a place of duty scoffed (8)
28 Daily spell shortened (4)
29 Solid capacity of Prohibition Act? (3,7)

DOWN

2 Where to see a version of one's death? (9)
3 Video from city showing game (5)
4 Allowance for dishonesty Alice repeatedly suffered? (9)
5 Academician to help a poor artist (7)
6 Less satisfactory rhyme for verse (5)
7 Fallen officer expired (9)
8 Use weapon to protect criminal (5)
14 Character in party had crashed in business (3,6)
16 Chose poor interpretation of heavenly plan (9)
17 Presiding officer, almost new, put up list of duties (9)
19 Like a yarn? Your old book is inside (7)
22 Feeling unwell, but head off depression (5)
23 Ambassador and staff hated king (5)
25 Puts down cross expressions of opinion (5)

ACROSS

1 Force politician into clumsy lie (5)
4 All hard cases in this family (9)
9 Sir Maurice? (9)
10 Fighting to terminate in knock-out (5)
11 How one may be evicted, in all cases? (3,3,7)
14 Too many bad workmen tend to blame it (4)
15 City copy for magazine (5,5)
18 Revolutionary quarter? (5,5)
19 Before conversion, his original character was different (4)
21 Cramped space in stifling billets (5,8)
24 Biblical character producing no end of a minor riot (5)
25 Pays for implement to make furniture (9)
27 Less gentle on each Oriental (9)
28 Joke targeted aunt (5)

DOWN

1 Cases of cultural development (10)
2 Writer of verse, not essay (3)
3 Discovers money makes money (6)
4 Problem afoot? Bill misplaced in sequence (9)
5 Remove covering from a European fiddle (5)
6 Prepare to fight to obtain knight's insignia (4,4)
7 Focus one's attention on money in box (11)
8 Eager to work in silver (4)
12 It was given to Maltese boatman on bridge (6,5)
13 *Bugsy Malone* production presenting no problems? (6,4)
16 Bad temper the result of sick jokes? (3,6)
17 Raise issue concerning volunteers? Never! (2,2,4)
20 Conservative turns up for crucial moments (6)
22 Delicate and charming female trapped by rising river (5)
23 One bent on submission (4)
26 Bird cry as heard in East End (3)

ACROSS

1 Sign for the swimming class (6)
5 Take advantage of easy win (8)
9 Put tar under vessel (8)
10 A couple of lines in atrocious poetry (6)
11 Mountain making German woman shrink at first (8)
12 Slowly going round a shed (6)
13 The early reform could be so tough (8)
15 Girl seized in enemy raid (4)
17 Learner in academic stream still (4)
19 Shaft mostly dark? Mostly (4-4)
20 Bird is spotted, sitting in hide (6)
21 Friar's dance scoffed at by schoolkids (4-4)
22 Recruit that's stationed near castle (6)
23 Be detained by one searching the ground for drink (4,4)
24 One looks after animals – a dog, if German (8)
25 'ad REM, possibly, towards end of night? (6)

DOWN

2 Bias not excluded by players' association (8)
3 Roman tyrant, one put by state over parts of Gaul (8)
4 Way to publicise crate's flight etc. (9)
5 Comfortable with large corporation? (4-11)
6 King oddly overlooking an extremely wicked activity (7)
7 Port – very alcoholic drink new to US agents (8)
8 In an amateurish way, one makes waves (5,3)
14 Uncordial characters that could threaten to stop play (4-5)
15 Sizes of hands and feet, say (8)
16 Puts a lot of stress on pen (4,4)
17 It's not usually usable *after* church (8)
18 Union leader in one mill organised material for shop floor, perhaps (8)
19 Rather faint ambition to secure success (7)

49

ACROSS

1   Mexican food Chileans 'ad cooked (10)
6   English company retains hard copy (4)
9   Nothing's freezing in this (10)
10 You'll find it in Perpendicular church (4)
12 Spoils of war? (4)
13 Be excessively trying (9)
15 Inclined to go without right education (8)
16 Fantastic runner legally ignoring all the odds (6)
18 Salad ingredient – in haste, it's left out (6)
20 Press has confused one about exhibit (8)
23 It's once or repeatedly mixed as perfume ingredient (5,4)
24 High cost of money once limiting motorway (4)
26 Associate could be friendly – but not at first (4)
27 Time for us, man, to grab popular gem (10)
28 What's potentially shocking about such corruption? (4)
29 Desire to treat wound for a certain party (5,5)

DOWN

1   Every item of fruit's a penny off (4)
2   Is able to get volunteers to repeat musical performance (7)
3   Dreadfully noisy cry said to be peculiar behaviour (12)
4   Flying first class, British entering right part of France (8)
5   Article portrayed Peter's brother (6)
7   Slaughter that's new in the era of the motorist? (7)
8   Work hard on the largely mistaken claim of viewer (10)
11 It's temporarily erected for pressing reasons (7,5)
14 People responsible for a full house (10)
17 Study of language that could bring one to richer translation (8)
19 Learning to get garland for alluring woman (7)
21 Man's masculine policy that limits skirt length (7)
22 Forming a circle around star, light a cigar (6)
25 Over the canal one can see a divine type (4)

ACROSS

1   Leaders of council here ashamed of such confusion (5)
4   Duplicity of tax every ruler introduced (9)
9   At worst a slave driver? (9)
10 Delicate and slender maiden drops out of treatment (5)
11 Where you see card's pips, at first glance (2,3,4,2,2)
14 23 stone – how fatty finishes up (4)
15 Fed up after grilling? (7,3)
18 Gratuitously provokes tinker (10)
19 Take wrong turning, get charged (4)
21 Settler – he isn't disposed to engage in controversy (5,3,5)
24 Extreme and difficult race in which to take part (5)
25 Seal again, after treatment giving relief from pain (9)
27 Nag parliamentarian to provide assistance for drivers (9)
28 Shrub in which bird is heard (5)

DOWN

1   Lords and ladies crazed by drink (6,4)
2   25's origins giving rise to gossip (3)
3   Son frequently exhibiting temper (6)
4   Work taken up by writer having no alternative? (9)
5   Spooky English lake (5)
6   It's easy to go round centre of Leeds – pedestrianised (8)
7   Modern technology used to reinterpret stone circle (11)
8   Toy – start off, and it repeatedly comes up (2-2)
12 Exactly how rent should be paid (2,3,6)
13 Sweet to eat that might improve the complexion (10)
16 Don't settle and dwell – it has strings attached (5,4)
17 Waterfall interminably tumbling – it's all part of the service (8)
20 Minor cut, perhaps (6)
22 River – every bit of it (5)
23 Book revealing what actually occurred? Not the first time (4)
26 Clout, for example (3)

51

ACROSS

1 Relax before conflict in plant (11)
7 For instance, goose's beginning (3)
9 One wanted to appear in this sort of picture (9)
10 Passion obvious in retrospective work (5)
11 Charms listeners on purpose (7)
12 Get too big for old hat to stretch (7)
13 Present daughter with a plaything outside (5)
15 Rich value in new make of car, say (9)
17 Some part, possibly, out of posh play (9)
19 They support speakers backing help to work (5)
20 Keep watch (7)
22 Be affected emotionally about horse going for slaughter (7)
24 I finish off a letter about one fool (5)
25 Older mounting (7,2)
27 Naval rating heading off tug suddenly (3)
28 Sweet maiden in Slough getting grant (11)

DOWN

1 Flowers to place in one's ear (3)
2 Maid of the Mountains with nothing to look at? (5)
3 Mouth opening here? What comes out could be true, say (7)
4 Assumes control and comes on to bowl (5,4)
5 Prayer Italian omitted in brief opening (5)
6 Wine in the Spanish clubs variable according to demand (7)
7 Got round English with strange riddle (9)
8 Aggressive action leading to widespread complaints (4,7)
11 Improvise without rate increase (11)
14 Butcher trims duck or chicken joint (9)
16 Pinned in by bishop, Scot chucked the game (9)
18 Slip on another one? (7)
19 Shakespearean heroine's pride at being transformed (7)
21 Anxious to get half-hearted West Indian music over (5)
23 Sort of cake for Tess's husband (5)
26 What would make women sign immediately? (3)

52

ACROSS

1 Disprove final parts of conjecture, however (5)
4 Usual MC in review lacking talent as singer (9)
9 Eccentric having to reduce, allowed vegetarian food (3,6)
10 This poet hates rhyme (unlike Keats) (5)
11 Shrub favoured by monarchs, perhaps (9,4)
14 Standard choice between central characters (4)
15 Link between premises created during spring at school? (6,4)
18 Animal expert and religious scholar moving East to West (10)
19 Book programme given backing, up to a point (4)
21 Widow, for example, can set tongues wagging (2,4,7)
24 Physician whose work was synonymous with organisation (5)
25 Reporter given hour in extra channel (4,5)
27 Way in which straight line cuts picture (9)
28 Benefactor's name displayed in entrance (5)

DOWN

1 With phone, bookmaker pages organiser (10)
2 Amount of information in book on computer studies (3)
3 Soundly instructed in French tense (6)
4 Inspirational, as 17 can be (9)
5 Graduate still upset fellow (5)
6 Old writers from America, viewed in characteristic ways (8)
7 Protection for rider the car's misdirected to steer into? (5,6)
8 Lavish drunkard (4)
12 Performer of light music? (5,6)
13 Representative of a thousand fish a fisherman got to rise (10)
16 Denial of responsibility somehow avoids law-breaking (9)
17 Alternative to flight from New York, say (8)
20 Soldiers reprimanded for spectacular bloomer (6)
22 Local in Gotham – a fool, it might appear (5)
23 Carriage drivers try to avoid (4)
26 You reported to navy vessel (3)

53

ACROSS

1 Boat needing reliable guide past Cape (7)
5 Business risks apparent in these books (7)
9 You are told Oxford course is held in only part of Oxford (5)
10 Family members returning rubbish to current supplier (9)
11 Youngster woman's held to be a beautiful child (6)
12 Head spy making trouble (8)
14 A land encountered in middle of sea passage (5)
15 Peak of classical poetry (9)
18 Payment method, being fashionable, suited one? (5,4)
20 Finish by executing guy (3,2)
22 Sounds interesting for youth – and for dad, apparently (3,5)
24 Better following horse (6)
26 Inspiring memories of detective's last case (9)
27 Move round to back of performing canine (5)
28 Crooked senator that's never prosperous? (7)
29 Not quite perfect chamber musician (7)

DOWN

1 Squeeze in economy left behind by high-fliers here? (4,5)
2 Censor material given to media – only one of two pages retained (7)
3 Pour out fast to get creamy head on stout (9)
4 Republican slogan? So classical! (4)
5 Mercury's position may be recorded by this Swedish astronomer's invention (10)
6 Men arrested by detectives fitted up in classical style (5)
7 Hazel's production caught by Tommy (7)
8 Lights up, seeing addition to letter (5)
13 Sudden entry of piano part I played (10)
16 A certain Pope – or one of several (9)
17 Maybe poor clues leave you extremely cold (9)
19 A small coin to assay? Okay (7)
21 Send wild, turning crimson with fury, nearly (7)
22 Appeal to bankrupt finally to fold (5)
23 Range of lead-free wall coverings (5)
25 Continue support (4)

ACROSS

1 *Variety* magazine welcomes book by one Times journalist (5,3)
6 Ingenious device not even guards see (6)
9 Weight going up and down a little bit with fashion (4,6)
10 Negative result of lack of exercise (4)
11 Frankfurter's ready in a roll, perhaps? (8,4)
13 Barmaid carried in the beer (4)
14 Row about infiltrating secret society somewhere in WI (8)
17 Shy fellow without wife gets depressed (4,4)
18 Fast food (4)
20 E.g. Haydn's work depicted in magazine letter thus (7,5)
23 Transport from Paddington, say (4)
24 Having abandoned hearth, do it? (3,3,4)
25 Change once made in republic by its leader (6)
26 Methods deployed to protect a premier (8)

DOWN

2 How lawyers write about ruling on part of army (2,2)
3 Makeshift old architectural feature's miles out (9)
4 Forge ahead and attack (4,2)
5 Start of final pronouncement in court (4,3,3,5)
6 How loveless singer upset composer (8)
7 Get bored looking up this material (5)
8 Cut most of text and upgrade novel (10)
12 Military unit's not getting involved (10)
15 One most insensitive about colour scheme's vulgarity (9)
16 Well organised in company (8)
19 Wrong maths answer leading to complaint (6)
21 Revolutionary who died in bloodbath (5)
22 City associated with extremely large country out East (4)

ACROSS

1 Young women good enough for writer (10)
6 Book that takes a couple of seconds (4)
9 I'm to carry out tests without new lab? Not bloody likely! (10)
10 Foreign woman cut crime (4)
12 Existing expenses (4,2,6)
15 Noble art patron well placed to see canvas (9)
17 Bow that originally had it (5)
18 Reported investigation of European country (5)
19 Work of Praxiteles, terribly atrophied (9)
20 Cave below one of the houses (5,7)
24 Out to lunch in clubs (4)
25 Runs into criminal simpleton getting bird (5,5)
26 Choice of large numbers for the rest of the pupils (4)
27 Light with shade? (6,4)

DOWN

1 Good old politician effortlessly making speech (4)
2 European has drink, finishing with the same again (4)
3 Challenge that place's visitors (3,4,5)
4 Cook a sort of meat (5)
5 Don't surrender stronghold when given hard offer (4,5)
7 Notes girl taking drink given by man (10)
8 Unpleasant bunch's dismissive attitude (4,6)
11 Money got from man in crew (5,2,5)
13 Where one can lie low (7-3)
14 War effort, initially, turned out submarine (10)
16 Hated faulty carriage – such a dangerous vehicle (5,4)
21 Young person's sort of suit (5)
22 Body of 6 turned over (4)
23 Magistrate has drugs put in military vehicle (4)

ACROSS

1 Special skill required with board game – it's very close (5-3-2)
7 Partner's decisive win (4)
9 The most powerful one in the game is female, however (8)
10 Half a dozen discards from hand allowed as well (3,3)
11 East the person bidding higher, we hear, in rubber (6)
12 How a chess game is likely to continue, many coaches take it (4,4)
13 Attempts to get card game under way (4)
15 Champion gets something to eat after game (10)
18 Draw with this line placed strategically (4,6)
20 Card-players' calls made in bridge, going towards West (4)
21 Cheat to secure a point in this game (8)
24 Deepest move initially is not worked out (6)
26 Small vehicle king used in game with skill (2-4)
27 Lots of drawing in this game (8)
28 Exploited ruse Diplomacy requires (4)
29 Player looking ahead gets start I bungled (10)

DOWN

2 Get opening pieces in Othello right, sage – or else! (9)
3 Lots of players making throws (5)
4 Bishop captured by powerful man on board – end of game's wonderful (9)
5 Energetically moving piece up in draughts, you invite counter, initially (7)
6 It's all right to take a pawn with one in this game (5)
7 Dealer giving one a king or queen? (9)
8 After shuffling a lot, new cards not dealt (5)
14 Piece of furniture not the central place for games? (9)
16 Run around to get number of bridge players needed in game (9)
17 Like Black and White, work both ways with positions (9)
19 With openings in chess, dared to go wrong? Hard cheese! (7)
22 More than one man in game cheats (5)
23 Poker bets made by opponents, say (5)
25 Giant first in Mastermind, extremely eager (5)

ACROSS

1 Witty remark's thrust divided province (6)
5 Highwayman almost returned to Hampstead area (8)
9 Terrify with a very powerful punch (8)
10 Boxer showing damage from massive hit (6)
11 Smiled at slip having dropped Jack, perhaps (8)
12 From which one is instructed what to do with libellous publication? (6)
13 Where guys are employed to put up temporary housing (4,4)
15 Get some shy person to talk up (4)
17 Barmaid serving shrub (4)
19 Shield from abuse, putting in a defence at last (8)
20 Gangster reached the island (3,3)
21 Odds on a helping of seconds (8)
22 Broadcaster's name relatively familiar? (6)
23 Not still uncomfortable indoors (8)
24 Behold game around Northern lake (4,4)
25 Protection for young boxers, say (6)

DOWN

2 With discrimination, as 18 would be portrayed? (8)
3 Litigating family bicker over new gamble, we hear (8)
4 Seven-stone pauper? (9)
5 Must admit aunt is transformed, when suitably changed (7,8)
6 Woman's clothes said to be poorly trimmed (7)
7 Appoint new ecclesiastical leader, a schismatic one (8)
8 Priceless treasures – millions removed from a single dwelling (8)
14 What currency traders may do that offers firm protection (9)
15 One that's drunk tainted social event (8)
16 Description of solid sort of relationship (8)
17 Unusual shape for half a pound of metal (8)
18 Woman coloured deeply, it's clear, when embraced by rough man (8)
19 It lengthened the tongue (7)

ACROSS

1 Where to find a partner for the mixed doubles? (8,6)
9 Dressed like one of our betters who has put everything on? (9)
10 Scholar's position has bearing on the church (5)
11 Proclaims a short piece from the Bible (5)
12 Contrived to play rough, say, with editor in court (7,2)
13 Remove basis for royalty (8)
15 Scandinavian article on smoked fish (6)
17 Detected merit in junior officer (6)
19 Sectarian quarrel holding local back (8)
22 Kitchen utensils used to make us canapés (9)
23 Trunk visitor somehow carries inside (5)
24 Agent changing last letter, or author's last few words (5)
25 Customers revealing limited intellect misused English (9)
26 How coach's pointing provides guidance for players (5,9)

DOWN

1 Keen preparation with 14 to provide dressing (7,7)
2 Train in torn old clothes (7)
3 Unnatural grimace right away shows stress (5)
4 Welcome from the waterworks (8)
5 Extra shot for golfer in the soup (6)
6 The quality of sound entertainment (9)
7 A troop operating in desert (7)
8 Very little happening when tide is low (4,2,3,5)
14 Paying for cover on house (9)
16 More luxurious place over the water accommodating alcoholic (8)
18 Drink a small volume during a stop (7)
20 Unfortunate king's held up by two from Mediterranean country (7)
21 Drove the Spanish hero off (6)
23 Pick me up, say, given unusually short notice (5)

59

ACROSS

1 Losing heart in opera, become strongly attached (4)
3 So-called queen next to king is normal (4)
6 Draw veil over couch to which one takes maiden (5)
10 Carpet salesman has to travel (7)
11 No actor may be seen in such a film (7)
12 Two commands in a meaningful sequence (4,5)
13 Swimmer last in heat – heavy defeat (5)
14 Junior person never running counter? (3-3)
16 Resistance in end, seen to weaken (8)
18 Survey showing nothing right inside, nothing right outside (4,4)
19 "Bow" rhymes with "row", possibly (6)
22 Film actor built up to quite a pitch? (5)
23 Model exam reply worked out (9)
25 Believed in faithful daughter – good man! (7)
26 Appease fool with talk of money to be earned (7)
27 Go gingerly with new driver in team (5)
28 Where one takes only seconds to receive honourable discharge (4)
29 It's a privilege to make the coffee (4)

DOWN

1 Dreamy physicist taking wife for daughter (7)
2 Extra pressure absorbed by litigant (5)
4 Meeting requirements, being mature and flexible (6)
5 Judge should allow no extremists to wreck peace (8)
6 How one unfairly dismissed could be satisfied immediately? (2,6,2,4)
7 Too darned stormy – something refreshing needed (9)
8 Aquatic mammal's partner eating an eel for starters (7)
9 In US, misrepresent a party project as threat to crop (8,6)
15 Under blanket, unable to move after fall (9)
17 Get dispatched by the block, as notepaper may (8)
18 Representatives refuse to hold up badge (7)
20 Painful condition of city overthrown in disaster (7)
21 Two auxiliaries perform well (6)
24 Calm down from a rage (5)

ACROSS

1   In direct confrontation – unlike Charles I in 1649 (4-2)
5   Lofty sort of view one may take of plant (5-3)
10 Drama featuring son and grandfather, perhaps (4)
11 At Christmas, most of us will be shown disapproval (3,3,4)
12 Bison appearing in erudite books (6)
13 Expert in converting disagreeable concoction back into drink (8)
14 Restaurant in which clubs wine and dine, entertained by song (9)
18 A long letter (5)
19 Gunman? (5)
20 Corolla's opening in flatter flower (9)
24 Wholeheartedly mixing love and duty (8)
25 Gun dogs (6)
26 Heir's due to dock and put down, according to report (10)
27 A side's joined the alliance (4)
28 Forcefully removing novice driver from sport (8)
29 Circular barrel in American gun (6)

DOWN

2   Strange things showing up in company tax that's fiddled (7)
3   Erase "p" in "empty" (7)
4   Garment that could be almost covering sleeper in US (7)
6   Travellers on the road may be experiencing problems (2,3,4)
7   Hurry up rate of progress – it's a long way away! (4,5)
8   Ambiguous quote about American spirit taken the wrong way (9)
9   Tree-bark displayed in office of church (9)
14 Mouthpiece giving source of heart attack? (6,3)
15 Following setback, energy is put into literary output (4,5)
16 Engine of war the heartless butcher deployed (9)
17 Rising level of noise following extremely rude celebrity (9)
21 Street light outside reveals barman (7)
22 Run into and split defence (7)
23 Opuntia growing wild in ideal state (7)

61

ACROSS

1 Resistance to mal de mer, say, among swimmers (3,4)
5 Sun-affected sailors slacken off (7)
9 Not a fellow to mix socially (9)
10 Teacher's pet endlessly seen (5)
11 Wild rose one found that's growing by the river (5)
12 Game to have a drink after the dance (9)
13 Proverbial labour saver (1,6,2,4)
17 Prince rather upset, having to accept a regal spouse (9,4)
21 Battle helmet (9)
24 Duplicator initially needs it to make copy (5)
25 Book a strong man (5)
26 Top-class doctor residing in modern flat (9)
27 Settles month and day (7)
28 Scene of constructive activity between Chinese banks (7)

DOWN

1 Dog had got inside plant (6)
2 He attacks with wild Alsatians (9)
3 Out of work, may one take it? (7)
4 Kind of Western food that's long in the cooking (9)
5 Exhaust advice about umbrellas in rain? (3,2)
6 A contest between two Poles and an Arab (7)
7 Inhuman character in book, heart-breaking (5)
8 Hesitated in speech, being handicapped (8)
14 Standing order's established in this system (9)
15 Going back to living quietly (2,7)
16 One who didn't strike Shakespeare as a sword carrier (8)
18 Covered a trial in the final stages (7)
19 Possibly bad sign for the corporation (7)
20 Courage to go to bank when cleaned out? (6)
22 Shrub is one in rising demand (5)
23 Through which Hamlet drove home his point (5)

ACROSS

1 One eye, say, kept on new baby's nightmares (6)
4 Dance craze used Coward's work (3,5)
10 Naturally, it powers a couple of rooms (5,4)
11 Laws of game not so short (5)
12 Change sides in discussion group to be so influential (7)
13 Port is offered by British to the left (7)
14 Objected to entering royal address – it's a matter of principle (4-10)
19 Idle pupil's view may be summarily rejected (3,2,3,6)
21 Vagrant has to carry one set of papers (7)
24 One who painted less well? Exactly! (7)
26 Direct flight to European capital (5)
27 No slouch hat? (9)
28 Assuming clothes may be spread on the bed (8)
29 Theologian has chapter at end of work to embellish (6)

DOWN

1 This month, one's in demand (6)
2 Journalist's charge about graduates losing head (9)
3 Aristocrat with lines in him showing up? (5)
5 Something nobody's prepared to say (2,3)
6 Stopped in Bedford after accident (9)
7 Lie in tub? Not I – I ran it, perhaps (5)
8 Anxious struggles – not with wife, but with son (8)
9 Almost what one hopes to hear from dowser? (4-4)
15 As pet, she's fun if played with (9)
16 Eats fish, with disagreeable consequences (8)
17 Free from old partner – divorce centre sent up a note (9)
18 Made up ground (8)
20 Run in the flesh? (6)
22 Pigs said to get thorough wash (5)
23 Use a blade and cut down tree (5)
25 Keep foot away from bomb hole, in case (5)

63

ACROSS

1 How extra-mural activities are heard about, it's said (5,4,4)
9 Confronted with hunger, looking sad (4-5)
10 Fabulous giant fish (5)
11 A second-class benefit (5)
12 Start to short circuit, and blow (4)
13 Spot in the middle of the ear (4)
15 Person honoured in upper chamber is academic (7)
17 Selfish attitude – even if disheartened (7)
18 One topping word game (7)
20 Mostly merry monarch, a tiny individual (7)
21 One part of hospital (4)
22 Facial expression showing mortification, having missed tea at first (4)
23 Run into front of car from another country (5)
26 Marriage using ring like the Piggy-Wig's (5)
27 Standard for e-mail messages originally different (9)
28 Guarding the joint, does it help to pack a powerful punch? (13)

DOWN

1 Eunuch wants gal? Strange conception of how things are (14)
2 Joins course (5)
3 Light relief from underground menace? (6,4)
4 Zola, for one, presenting a volume to employer (7)
5 Final part of board meeting staged by Beckett (7)
6 Leader of faction dismissed as culturally pretentious (4)
7 A travesty of justice in two sporting events (4,5)
8 Be short of currency in speculation – always the shady businessman (5,9)
14 Like the best French courses (6,4)
16 How a drink transforms what one makes (9)
19 County man brought up family (7)
20 Such strength in steel, especially (7)
24 Raise Watch Committee's scope of authority (5)
25 In this country, two-thirds read (4)

ACROSS

1 Carpenter, for one, producing a flier (6-7)
9 Excursion on which one pleases oneself? (3,4)
10 Sort of fly with rook or another bird (7)
11 Small island church coming to its end (5)
12 Opener in county's team (9)
13 Verse, perhaps, that gives one something to remember (8)
15 Unusually large and troublesome delivery (6)
18 Revise poem by unknown at Scottish festival (6)
19 Flourishes ticket money for football followers (8)
22 How one deals with foot-faults in service (9)
24 Manner of performing steps, say (5)
25 Typical example of back exercises one found heavy work (7)
26 Serving a portion of food (7)
27 Journalist runs into person cited in court case (13)

DOWN

1 Amass too many weapons for normal method of delivery in the field (7)
2 Winning measure from brusque person in charge (5,4)
3 Listening device covering most of the ground (5)
4 Friar's broken china cup (8)
5 Rower's bench made from block (6)
6 Difficult to fill with food and liquor (4,5)
7 Love at first sight admitted by one who regrets being king (5)
8 Backslider in the Cabinet, perhaps? (6)
14 Unwell, having bad complexion (3,6)
16 Strange interplay in a shared service (5,4)
17 Title of his play composed about daughter (8)
18 Mouse taken to guy (6)
20 Deceptive movement brings vehicle in on time (7)
21 Fuse has explosive in the middle (6)
23 "Hippy" found in Brazilia cadging (5)
24 Wise man of old cut short farewell (5)

ACROSS

1   Again eating mushroom to build up muscle (6)
4   Old embassy's oversight (8)
10 Instrument for off-peak calls (9)
11 Popular song about king (5)
12 Wind's backing visible in photograph of open sea (7)
13 Without cover from air, thus exposed on Yorkshire moor (7)
14 See new driver tear off further down the road (5)
15 Get wind of Daisy in cathedral city (8)
18 Feature of Susan's mouse (5,3)
20 Come about small volume in our keeping (5)
23 Expression used by drinkers for so long (7)
25 Red-hot stuff from South American capital (7)
26 Master using king to take knight (5)
27 He impresses with his colourful technique (9)
28 With spin on ball, approaches obliquely (8)
29 Vehemently criticise very musical line (6)

DOWN

1   Tall thin supporter of runners (8)
2   Pet about to whimper in plagued house (7)
3   Praying with Church of England, composed words of praise (9)
5   United rivals developing synthetic cream (10,4)
6   Left suddenly broke into factions (5)
7   One new computer unit beneficially provides desktop writing aid (7)
8   Lack of medication for swelling (6)
9   Hard lines? (8,6)
16 English horse second to American named after famous person (9)
17 Translate English or Latin into Chinese, for example (8)
19 Pull fish up on one side of boat (7)
21 Tip given in a wine bar (7)
22 Balance plates of fish (6)
24 Frenchman and wife to make a fresh start (5)

66

ACROSS

1 Only some MPs welcome call for help to provide work for the young (4,2,7)
9 About to smear name in tabloid? Painful effect of overexposure (7)
10 Middle section of Jean Genet novel describing youth (7)
11 Final change, in a manner of speaking, is silly (5)
12 Actor's application will face rejection (6,3)
13 Reviled outlaw leader, perhaps (8)
15 Important woman banned union (6)
18 Out of bed and ready to go abroad, say (6)
19 Plant or animal associated with grand passion (8)
22 A load of software (9)
24 Officer and Duke cut off king's escape (5)
25 Severely practical female foresakes vanity (7)
26 Hostility only voiced in private, say (7)
27 Leader of military attack getting all-out effort? (7,6)

DOWN

1 Plant with flowers just opening – like the one I own? (7)
2 Quick to respond, as event is repeatedly moving (9)
3 Plump for an illegal occupation (5)
4 Left home after being smothered by one of the family (8)
5 Team kit (6)
6 Making a record also requires one with pizazz (9)
7 Make use of some rancorous language (5)
8 Meet in Kent area and get married in cathedral city (6)
14 Breaking down after getting a bellyful (9)
16 I riot, for a change, for a more compelling cause (1,8)
17 "Gosh", platoon leader said – or one of his men? (8)
18 Nurse drops heroin in secluded spot (6)
20 Back last runner, not first (7)
21 One who'll settle, seizing right chance (6)
23 Old place for circus seal (1-4)
24 Painter getting up well before noon (5)

ACROSS

1 Check with soldiers stationed in keep (6)
4 Top people – Edward Lear or Henry James, for example? (8)
10 An inferior story in US produces humiliation (9)
11 Quick article liable to be shocking (5)
12 A person emphatically feels no different (7)
13 The sort of dealings one may have truck with (7)
14 Self-satisfied declaration of my errorless performance to sailor? (2,3,5,4)
19 Layout of art in Acropolis is intriguing (14)
21 For her, pride is the issue (7)
24 Occupied as one intended (7)
26 Epic poem newspapers pointlessly rejected (5)
27 Refreshments and other supplies originally taken out of flat (9)
28 Produce information with energy and speed (8)
29 Social classes backed at faculty meeting (6)

DOWN

1 Work out in the grounds (6)
2 New mart needs retail dealers (9)
3 Goddess supplying some dire necessities (5)
5 Suitable work for milkmaids? (5)
6 Mineral from lake thrown over plant (9)
7 It's a bit steep, exposing 29? (5)
8 Appropriate party food for children? (8)
9 Fisherman, perhaps – one observing catches at a distance (8)
15 What one visually interprets, we hear (3-6)
16 Like smocking, it's inferred (8)
17 Pain relief when leg's broken in a northern part of the world (9)
18 Sailors initially gathering for water sport (8)
20 Poem written on ship overlooking a port (6)
22 He hunted immediately after imbibing port (5)
23 Charming composition we hear (5)
25 Fellow taking wicket for county (5)

ACROSS

1 Untidy person's first to change for dance (9)
6 Resonant sound central to exotic languages (5)
9 National emblem included in the new list (7)
10 Mischievous falsehood uttered when identifying these molluscs (7)
11 Middle Eastern country's urge to capture Eastern state (5)
12 Citadel's produce grown in a loose soil (9)
13 It leads some creatively into future imagined (3-2)
14 One spotted with a hundred others in the cinema (9)
17 Fly round centre of lake – or sail (9)
18 Very old woman leading round of applause (5)
19 It came in damaged about midnight? How puzzling (9)
22 Plain-spoken canon (5)
24 A rise to accommodate the workers (7)
25 Unauthorised backing for prisoner with sick note (7)
26 Gang's hidden money, say (5)
27 Take off quickly and fly, in seat (9)

DOWN

1 Mole that's black and extremely tiny (5)
2 A crowd of men in office? (9)
3 Prolongation of strained relations with former partner (9)
4 Things knocked back for pleasure (4,3,8)
5 Common procedure providing Watson with cases (7,8)
6 Tramp added support to boot (5)
7 Spirit of article that's side-splitting (5)
8 Sings do ... la, perhaps, in this? (9)
13 Englishman demanding upbeats in military band (9)
15 Diggers are regularly employed on its soil (9)
16 Misguided as Dreyfus was? (3-6)
20 Lay to rest Doolittle's suspicion of woman (5)
21 Puzzling situation when one stands amid alien corn (5)
23 Search thoroughly, having dropped meal ticket in river (5)

ACROSS

1 More than a little like Caesar's wife? (5,9)
9 Embarrassed, given clearly guilty (3-6)
10 Repeat bow and leave the stage right away (5)
11 Beak accepting old form of capital punishment (5)
12 Flowing oil in USA area – here? (9)
13 Paper, in small pieces, covering union negotiators (8)
15 Threaten to make naughty child stop (6)
17 Flora gets into bed (6)
19 Maybe saint is rejected by bishop in old college (8)
22 How one pays immediately as the hammer falls (2,3,4)
23 Carry on putting tea, say, in appropriate place (3,2)
24 Run over the same piece of music (5)
25 Outgoing type of dog in former times (9)
26 Foolish persons ended extremely coldly in Antarctic region (4,10)

DOWN

1 Dries gradually replace wets, so to speak, in such a cabinet (6,8)
2 Dated Cynthia? Just a phase she's going through (3,4)
3 Proud pair dismissed by bishop, perhaps (5)
4 Wave's excessive, covering half of land over time (8)
5 General dislike associated with power base (6)
6 Upset monarchists on leaving this festival (9)
7 Shock right in the middle of break in electricity supply (7)
8 Compassionate leaves? (3,3,8)
14 Something we got from the French in confidence (5,4)
16 Putting hindrance in way of gambling activity (8)
18 Merchant foolishly a pound in debt (7)
20 One bird attacked another with beak (7)
21 Bargain offer includes ends of pine timber (6)
23 Not having, for example, a heart bypass (5)

70

ACROSS

1 In the same position, showing no emotion (7)
5 Working on a motorway, so providing diversion (7)
9 Quickly departs when it's time to retire (6,3)
10 Fleece providing warmth when there's cold front (5)
11 Coin King Henry initially presented to female (4-9)
13 Another mathematical term for triangle that's not right (8)
15 Garment put on Emma, for example (6)
17 Old woman serving Americans ethnic food (6)
19 Highest point reached by salt in tree (8)
22 Remarkable addition to coat of arms? (13)
25 One piece of sausage removed for casserole (5)
26 It puts everyone into a house (9)
27 Lying absurdly about high tension as play is performed? (7)
28 If a sailor returns, have a drink (7)

DOWN

1 Pronounced fruit so unlike a peach! (4)
2 Picture result of pouring in tea? (7)
3 Living in very restricted part of Europe (5)
4 Reckoning occasion's so odd, and may become crazy (8)
5 Vigorous middle age, according to Jaques? Point taken (6)
6 Primarily chancy in nature, perhaps (9)
7 With rocks, the best equipment climber can have (3-4)
8 Safety instructions to mountaineers bringing angry response? (3,7)
12 Main area available in July and August? (4,6)
14 Musician's variation on air after it is taken up by wind (9)
16 One's entered the church (8)
18 Support with crowd, being at top of table (7)
20 Keen to bolt, cause unnecessary alarm (3,4)
21 Put house in order (6)
23 A short piece of poetry in circulation (5)
24 She's tucked into army rations (4)

71

ACROSS

1 Take a retrograde step and cheat when selling car? (3,4,3,5)
9 Previous incumbent comes back in place of rector, initially (9)
10 One entitled to have new order accepted by soldiers (5)
11 Child repeatedly turned back animal (3-3)
12 Slyly look at a work that's incomplete, easy to see through (8)
13 Spy chief is to attack unsuitable worker (6)
15 Scottish author given a hearing in town across border (8)
18 Weapon, possibly mine (8)
19 American beauty queen becoming wife? (6)
21 Eventually getting a ton on board – it's very close (8)
23 From stage I shall remove this female entertainer (6)
26 For example, turning back cover can make one cold (5)
27 Measure by legal authority enclosed area (9)
28 Bob disappeared when this was launched on D-day (7,8)

DOWN

1 Way Father is elevated to highest position open to him? (7)
2 Finely tune television, initially faint (5)
3 Element – the second I kept in here (not in US) (9)
4 Something not experienced by Miss Beale – or Buss? (4)
5 Male carried by roan he's broken, perhaps (8)
6 Criminal caught going over castle (5)
7 Thinks nothing, initially, about writer in public transport (9)
8 Entertaining result of performing bars of music (7)
14 Such a show-off crams late, perhaps (5,4)
16 Dudley's a place in the Midlands (9)
17 Formal procedures giving support to officer (8)
18 Cowered, surrounded by a large number of Romans (7)
20 Support ready for immediate use (5-2)
22 Precocious girl married the first man to appear (5)
24 Offspring – son produced by pop (5)
25 Influential teacher you are said to find in good university (4)

ACROSS

1   Sort of publication that's repeatedly stern (8)
6   Decline father's drink (4,2)
9   Covering material that's used by church (6)
10 What brings end of true distinction? (8)
11 Artist's animal held back by prior arrangement (8)
12 Old lady of Paris taking man to island (6)
13 Animal that's vicious in the extreme? Precisely! (5)
14 Mysterious things may be spotted in his study (9)
17 Hit difficulty providing illumination (9)
19 Hard-hearted king called for composer (5)
22 Wife's turn to complain peevishly (6)
23 Environmentalist knowing there's a threat to vegetation (8)
24 Man's surrounded by it (5,3)
25 Steal article that is very minimally protected? (6)
26 Poet's love evident in great composition (6)
27 Female disposing of shells near here? It's hard to say (8)

DOWN

2   He finds it hard to believe that he is taking part (7)
3   Fruit to pack – this will record when (4,5)
4   A support for vessel coming out of the water (6)
5   Stick to path laid down and don't take drug? (4,3,3,5)
6   If you want to stay in Bath, stop it! (8)
7   Incentives limit us in a strange way (7)
8   Cash dispenser appears to make young man tarry (9)
13 Game so poor before this replacement (4,5)
15 The village of Gotham (9)
16 One likes pictures from the Orient – awfully nice frames (8)
18 Male doing poorly in post (7)
20 A line written to sweetheart covering everything (3-4)
21 Situation offered to a big gun, so-called (6)

ACROSS

1 Amerind we see quietly following fawn (5)
4 Horrid ruling cops backed up (9)
9 Duck's catch, going round in pond and river (9)
10 Loots and boots out (5)
11 Small bird feeling pain, having wings clipped (6)
12 Happy tap dancing with poise (8)
14 Inspired zany on cue acted furiously (10)
16 Red meat or grouse (4)
19 Distinguished opener in tests practised (4)
20 A break in exercise, it seems (10)
22 Man (model soldier?) halting (8)
23 Jam spread thinly on bread (6)
26 Part in *Twelfth Night* – one playing it takes a bow (5)
27 Are bananas, in conclusion, sweet? (9)
28 Smash hit, a crass release (9)
29 Menace turning out hard to handle (5)

DOWN

1 Cheese, in part, eaten by puss (9)
2 Panic, losing head, and slip (5)
3 A metal among the best? (8)
4 Fly by waterside plant (4)
5 Marginal leader in pentathlon, top Olympian in danger (10)
6 Boasting cheat and braggart (6)
7 Metamorphosis of Circe, that designing person (9)
8 Sample what a steak can provide (5)
13 Workers in wood parking in vehicle with logs (10)
15 Junior's to pay for bloomer (9)
17 Wrestler, perhaps, clever to hang on to the ear (9)
18 Inclination to write song (8)
21 Start, in slightly poor shape, on first of aerobic classes (6)
22 Nearly all experience officer commanding destruction (5)
24 Brook having fish given higher rating (5)
25 Sums up commercials as sound (4)

ACROSS

1 Chosen pieces as arranged by one composer or another (10)
7 Springs in a convulsive movement cut short (4)
10 A sudden descent on the organ? (4-4)
11 No solicitor dismissed? On the contrary (3,3)
12 Tenant bound by rules seemingly (6)
13 Black stuff on outside of cloth is aromatic herb (8)
15 Lecherous look from bravo grabbing first of girls (4)
16 I get to slip badly and flap on the way down (10)
18 Horrible Vera bit Pam, beastly type drawing blood (7,3)
21 A trained educationist retired (4)
22 Personal appeal, so tea is laid by Mum (8)
24 Happen to suffer restriction in hearing (6)
25 Experienced trainer brings fellows to peak (6)
26 Don't put defender on transfer list – could be reserve (4,4)
27 Final help here for a pair down on their uppers? (4)
28 Find me in such a state, reverse of healthy old person (10)

DOWN

2 Work out steps for hop or charge around clumsily (11)
3 Perhaps maidens given shelter gently slumber through the day? (9)
4 Artlessness of bridge player I've scoffed about (7)
5 The answer for someone wanting to be 21 but lacking the bottle? (8,7)
6 Officer not concerned with details (7)
8 Bit of implement – for turning over ends of garden? (5)
9 Findin' place for protest (3-2)
14 Judge's comments that could be diatribe to Counsel, primarily (6,5)
17 Easily controlled vehicle going up on plateau (9)
19 Stage offering rock – half of it guitar sound (7)
20 Bill not high, it's reported, for a spectacular show (7)
22 Arrived with new driver in desert transport (5)
23 Name a long time around (5)

ACROSS

1 Priest with a couple of Bishops, heading East (4)
3 A sign of love that's sweet (4)
6 Pay tribute to a good person (5)
10 Get runs in match, that is plain (7)
11 Have an ambition that helps the other side (3,4)
12 Sort of wall that could be made in granite (9)
13 Arrested for quarrel (3-2)
14 Carrier? This ship's smaller (6)
16 Irritates son, being redundant (8)
18 Extension of loan, say, with a lot of banknotes extra (4-4)
19 Church worker coming from Essex to Norfolk (6)
22 Miss a green – up in arms (5)
23 Amplifies how amusement shows on one's face (9)
25 Injured grabbing one in second half for United (7)
26 Powerful relation (7)
27 Present of plaything a daughter held back (5)
28 Well done? By no means uncommon (4)
29 Each one, except the first, is jolly (4)

DOWN

1 Gear engineers installed in alarm (7)
2 Leaf caught in child's grip (5)
4 Capital taken from African country lands in Western Europe (6)
5 Berkshire town's top journalist is discarded (8)
6 Large cask writer provided after game in Kentish town (9,5)
7 Decking put Navy crew in a spot (9)
8 Gifts of money once (7)
9 Act of worship with Holy Writ, perhaps, in admirable way (14)
15 Information about long-established staff in plant (6,3)
17 Reduce tameness of puzzle (8)
18 Allow in again to study with American college (7)
20 Lack of influence about, say, a bunch of flowers (7)
21 Dreadful score test opener got – a duck (6)
24 Point lace (5)

ACROSS

1 Sign showing note in foreign currency (5)
4 Making dreadful scene, tend to be condemned (9)
9 Gang from Irish town means to get at the drink (9)
10 Guided around in the morning, being disabled (5)
11 Publication that describes lots (4,9)
14 One needs nothing, thanks, or very little (4)
15 Musical group stepping out together (6,4)
18 It enables one to get the message – after reflection, naturally (10)
19 This false witness could turn to abuse (4)
21 Question put by examiners? Fancy that! (4,2,3,4)
24 Returning, achieved apparently very good times (5)
25 Where flock is fed, with help so badly needed (9)
27 Suspend sailor from window? Stop! (4,5)
28 It may be drawn or sucked up (5)

DOWN

1 Love to laugh at these security workers? (10)
2 Keep out of the company of lawyers (3)
3 Lorraine's companion in France (6)
4 Rack for litter (9)
5 A column in flight (5)
6 Speak highly of English record one established in employment (8)
7 Contest the capitalistic principle (11)
8 They're assumed to be failures (4)
12 Children's story – I'm to tell new version (6,5)
13 Operatic lady happy to be left on her own? (5,5)
16 Concerning an empty form needed to get compensation (9)
17 Reproduction of a man's oil painting (4,4)
20 Disorder in Parliament once ruling over us (6)
22 Place to dance in a girl's company (5)
23 Attack the copper with acid (4)
26 Blade used by a cutter, perhaps (3)

ACROSS

1   Play for famous actor, such as The Apple Cart? (7)
5   Editor's failing with circulation (7)
9   Sign of greedy anticipation that loses one deliverance (9)
10 Class A drug (5)
11 Mainstream rock means to progress (8,5)
13 Exploit complete year in an effective manner (8)
15 Warms a cold piece from breast of turkey, say (3,3)
17 Advances stealthily and steals coin away (6)
19 Scoff following footballer's low position (4,4)
22 Support the starter, say, and last out (4,3,6)
25 What bad librettist keeps improvising (2,3)
26 Labour might produce red workers here? (9)
27 Dropping Ecstasy – close to prison (7)
28 Aquatic plant duck's taken only once in blue moon, oddly (7)

DOWN

1   There's no time to view entry permit (4)
2   Completely heard witness in this court (4,3)
3   Poor sister left in anxiety (5)
4   Way-out political forecaster? (4,4)
5   Current cause of unsettled weather (2,4)
6   Instrument's sound in *The Clock* and part of *The Hen*? (9)
7   One member with records of debt far from good (7)
8   Caught in dreadful tragedy in model community (6,4)
12 Supporter displaying the score (5,5)
14 Bound to win if bishop's sacrificed, so not to be gobbled up (9)
16 Pig's extended nap (8)
18 Film star getting place in series (7)
20 Woman's a bad actor – it's some way from Stratford (7)
21 Salt, a product of the ocean (6)
23 Wild animal's length to estimate first (5)
24 Operation turned up work for colleague (4)

78

ACROSS

1 Bird behind tobacco plant (8,7)
9 Girl receives prize – a port (3,6)
10 Dull report Conservative presented to Parliament once (5)
11 A loose woman in the family (6)
12 Could our genes make us liberal like this? (8)
13 Girl left as usual (6)
15 Produce conviction – time to regret joining gang (4,4)
18 Composer bringing back character such as Figaro, initially (8)
19 Girl one may get out of breath (6)
21 Breathing space given part of orchestra – flute, perhaps (8)
23 Completely fascinated by outskirts of Tokyo (2,4)
26 Scouts having disappointing time on way back (5)
27 Being tactful, I'd comply with a reform (9)
28 Home replay, with minor changes, in European section (4,5,6)

DOWN

1 Criminal's house and home (7)
2 Get bow ready – Robin's had change of heart (5)
3 One elderly relative, one friend – how dull! (9)
4 Bit of verse from William Blake (4)
5 Superficially improving Greek island – alien given some rights by Greeks (8)
6 There's talk of a medal for Earl Marshal, for example (5)
7 Dives as dog runs into another pet (9)
8 Sally, soprano caught up in ceremonial (7)
14 Musical entertainment with a sort of cake and bread (4,1,4)
16 Cast preen and preen again, after opening, in here? (5,4)
17 The state of fatherhood that's attained by Asian breadwinner? (8)
18 Accompany round clubs, gaining entrance (7)
20 Dreadful annoyed, this is soothing (7)
22 Article that poses a number of questions (5)
24 Approval bestowed on a good animal (5)
25 Short drive speeds up (4)

ACROSS

1 Monarch rejected hatred – that's a relief (7)
5 Form of protection favoured by soldier (7)
9 French vineyard and French wine bottle (5)
10 One beer ain't enough, perhaps for him (9)
11 Piece of rock – dashed for cover (6)
12 Greedy with hunger, I use rent improperly (8)
14 One French man and woman (5)
15 Scared of outsiders, one withdraws from other races (9)
18 One may be pushed to admit a late entry (5-4)
20 Addition to book for teachers' training (5)
22 Confusing viewers with brilliance (8)
24 Containing loose stones with pole, wire netting (6)
26 Yanks operate these to summon help (4-5)
27 Play on green with one's cherubic children (5)
28 I do business extremely lucratively in optimal circumstances (7)
29 That woman was vulgar in low drinking dive (7)

DOWN

1 Quality of pictures in hotel foyer (9)
2 Start to slip and fall? (7)
3 Rational judgment seen in, say, shock treatment (9)
4 Send off part of remittance required (4)
5 Amicably changing sides just before the end would be a joke (10)
6 The bloodier the better (5)
7 To identify unpleasant smell is not a cure (7)
8 Negotiate for free entertainment (5)
13 Former partner gets the bird inside and outside (10)
16 Fundamental truth star proclaimed (9)
17 Another line put in granny flat, for example (9)
19 Look around 'orrible place for antelope (7)
21 Put up with change he hates (7)
22 Name excellent sheikhdom (5)
23 Gently wash the Spanish jacket part (5)
25 One little sibling is a divine creature (4)

80

ACROSS

1 To avoid danger, eat only eggs now? (4,4,5)
9 Briefly held what Cleopatra fatally grasped in embrace (7)
10 In dismay about costume (7)
11 Australian river backing up produces impressive display (5)
12 Taking in sailors and soldiers with talent (9)
13 Proverbially lifeless stud (8)
15 Temporary relief from wild plant? Not always (6)
18 Deny outside is blue (6)
19 Broadcast route covers motorway (8)
22 Person keeping a discount in error (9)
24 Dough essential to keep a stable (5)
25 Ice does, when it re-forms – see! (7)
26 To show veneration to girl is prostrate when speaking (7)
27 Hold official enquiry into boundary hedge (3,2,3,5)

DOWN

1 Caterer showing cook a short way (7)
2 Ministers going round one university instead of another (9)
3 Ability to express nothing risqué (5)
4 Prominence of ecstasy and speed in current circumstances (8)
5 Cook sounds like an ass, we hear (6)
6 Initially causing a stir about a cover for horse (9)
7 What's in this bottle? Never rum (5)
8 Bachelor, lissom and light-hearted (6)
14 Shape of Western woodland (3,6)
16 Granting access (9)
17 Wave foreign money in error (8)
18 Deliver verdict, clearing one from unholy crime (6)
20 Gymnastic equipment teacher's beginning to demolish outside gym lesson (7)
21 Hog a lot of time available for business (6)
23 Hammock used aboard ship – from Glasgow, perhaps (5)
24 Academic concealing old evidence (5)

THE SOLUTIONS

SOLUTIONS

1

R O S E ■ I S I S ■ T O P U P
E ■ K ■ B ■ A ■ N U ■ A R
B O U Q U E T ■ A I N T R E E
U ■ L ■ S U P ■ B ■ T ■ B
F U L L M A R K S ■ R H Y M E
F ■ A ■ N ■ H ■ I ■ L ■ N
S A V A N T ■ W O O D W I N D
■ I ■ S E T ■ T ■ G ■ N
B A C K H A N D ■ R E C E S S
E ■ E ■ O ■ G ■ S ■ W ■ ■ I
N A V E L ■ O N T H E B A L L
E ■ E ■ I ■ R ■ A ■ L ■ M E
F I R E D O G ■ B A L L O O N
I ■ S ■ A ■ E ■ L ■ S U ■ C
T R A C Y ■ D I E T ■ U R G E

2

M O C K T U R T L E ■ K I N G
O ■ A ■ U ■ A ■ I ■ H ■ R ■ W
B A K E R ■ C E N T E N A R Y
S ■ E ■ K ■ K ■ E ■ A ■ Q ■ N
T E S T I F I E D ■ V O I C E
E ■ T ■ S ■ N ■ U ■ I ■ ■ D
R O A D H O G ■ P L E A D E D
■ N ■ D ■ ■ ■ R ■ O ■
S A D N E S S ■ T A T T L E R
L ■ L ■ O ■ E ■ H ■ C ■ E
A S S A I ■ P R E V A L E N T
M ■ H ■ G ■ R ■ H ■ N ■ V ■ R
M A R C H H A R E ■ A L I C E
E ■ E ■ T ■ N ■ E ■ I ■ T ■ A
D O D O ■ W O N D E R L A N D

3

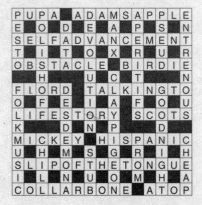

P U P A ■ A D A M S A P P L E
E ■ O ■ D ■ E ■ A ■ P ■ S ■ N
S E L F A D V A N C E M E N T
T ■ I ■ T ■ O ■ X ■ R ■ U ■ R
O B S T A C L E ■ B I R D I E
■ H ■ U ■ C ■ T ■ N
F I O R D ■ T A L K I N G T O
O ■ F ■ E ■ I ■ A ■ F ■ O ■ U
L I F E S T O R Y ■ S C O T S
K ■ D ■ N ■ P ■ D
M I C K E Y ■ H I S P A N I C
U ■ H ■ M ■ S ■ G ■ R ■ I ■ H
S L I P O F T H E T O N G U E
I ■ L ■ N ■ U ■ O ■ M ■ H ■ A
C O L L A R B O N E ■ A T O P

4

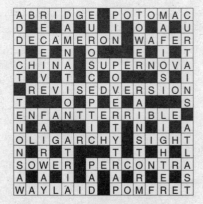

A B R I D G E ■ P O T O M A C
D ■ E ■ A ■ U ■ I ■ O ■ A ■ U
D E C A M E R O N ■ W A F E R
I ■ E ■ N ■ O ■ ■ E ■ I ■ T
C H I N A ■ S U P E R N O V A
T ■ V ■ T ■ C ■ O ■ S ■ I
■ R E V I S E D V E R S I O N
T ■ O ■ P ■ E ■ A ■ S
E N F A N T T E R R I B L E ■
N ■ A ■ I ■ T ■ N ■ I ■ A
O L I G A R C H Y ■ S I G H T
N ■ R ■ T ■ T ■ T ■ H ■ L
S O W E R ■ P E R C O N T R A
A ■ A ■ I ■ A ■ A ■ R ■ E ■ S
W A Y L A I D ■ P O M F R E T

5

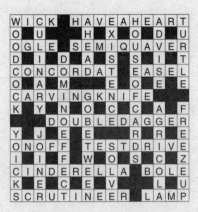

6

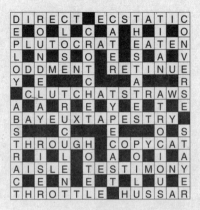

7

8

SOLUTIONS

9

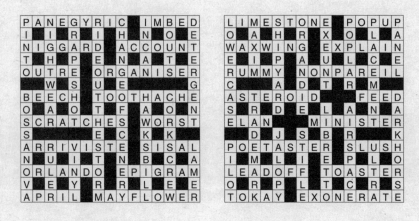

10

11

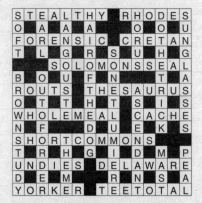

12

13

C	A	R	D	S	H	A	R	P			B	E	B	O	P
L		U		T		R		R		A		O		E	
A	R	G	U	E		O	B	E	I	S	A	N	C	E	
S		B		V		U		C		I		A		L	
S	H	Y	N	E	S	S		E	L	L	I	P	S	E	
I			D		E	D				A				R	
F	O	R	G	O	O	D	M	E	A	S	U	R	E		
Y		O		R				W		T				S	
	S	U	P	E	R	C	O	N	T	I	N	E	N	T	
A		N			A		E		N					I	
R	A	D	D	L	E	D		B	A	B	Y	L	O	N	
D			H	A	D		U		U		E			G	
O	V	E	R	S	P	I	L	L		R	A	V	E	R	
U		A		S		S		A		N		E		A	
R	O	D	E	O		H	O	R	S	E	P	L	A	Y	

14

F	A	B	R	I	C		A	P	E	R	I	T	I	F
	P		A		A		R		E		R		L	
S	P	E	C		T	A	K	E	I	T	E	A	S	Y
	A		K		C		S		A		D		W	
B	R	E	E	C	H		P	E	D	I	C	U	R	E
	E		T		U		N		N		C		I	
P	L	A	Y	A	P	A	R	T		E	Y	I	N	G
O		N		S		F		E		R		N		H
L	E	G	I	T		F	O	R	E	S	I	G	H	T
I		E		R		L		N		G		O		
S	Y	L	L	A	B	U	S		V	A	N	D	A	L
H		I		D		E		E		O		R		
O	C	C	I	D	E	N	T	A	L		B	O	D	Y
F		A		L		C		O		L		E		
F	A	L	T	E	R	E	D		P	O	E	T	R	Y

15

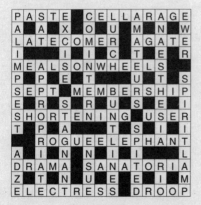

P	A	S	T	E		C	E	L	L	A	R	A	G	E
A		A		X		O		U		M		N		W
L	A	T	E	C	O	M	E	R		A	G	A	T	E
I			I		I		C		T		E			R
M	E	A	L	S	O	N	W	H	E	E	L	S		
P		P		E		T		U		T		S		
S	E	P	T		M	E	M	B	E	R	S	H	I	P
E		R		S		R		U		S		E		I
S	H	O	R	T	E	N	I	N	G		U	S	E	R
T		P		A		T		S		I		I		I
		R	O	G	U	E	E	L	E	P	H	A	N	T
A		I		N		N		I		I				L
D	R	A	M	A		S	A	N	A	T	O	R	I	A
Z		T		N		U		E		E		I		M
E	L	E	C	T	R	E	S	S		D	R	O	O	P

16

M	A	R	M	O	T		C	A	N	A	I	L	L	E
	G		A		E		L		O		G		E	
B	R	O	K	E	N	D	O	W	N		L	I	F	T
	E		E		A		U		U		O		T	
R	E	A	S	O	N	E	D		S	P	O	T	O	N
		H		T		C		A		V			V	
M	A	L	I		U	N	G	L	O	V	E	D		
	G		F		B		C		E		F		R	
B	O	A	T	H	O	O	K			F	I	S	T	
N				T		O		S		T				
B	Y	P	A	S	S		O	V	E	R	H	A	N	G
	A		R		W		L		N		E		Y	
B	U	N	G		A	D	A	M	S	A	P	P	L	E
	N		O		N		N		O		E		O	
S	T	A	N	D	A	R	D		R	E	G	E	N	T

17

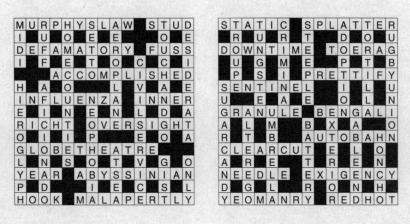

M	U	R	P	H	Y	S	L	A	W		S	T	U	D
I		U		O		E		E				O		E
D	E	F	A	M	A	T	O	R	Y		F	U	S	S
I		F		E		T		O		C		C		I
		A	C	C	O	M	P	L	I	S	H	E	D	
H		A		O			L		V		A		E	
I	N	F	L	U	E	N	Z	A		I	N	N	E	R
E		I		N		E		N		L		D		A
R	I	C	H	T		O	V	E	R	S	I	G	H	T
O		I		I		P			E		O		A
G	L	O	B	E	T	H	E	A	T	R	E			
L		N		S		O		T		V		G		O
Y	E	A	R		A	B	Y	S	S	I	N	I	A	N
P		D			I		E		C		S		L
H	O	O	K		M	A	L	A	P	E	R	T	L	Y

18

S	T	A	T	I	C		S	P	L	A	T	T	E	R
	R		U		R		T		D		O		U
D	O	W	N	T	I	M	E		T	O	E	R	A	G
	U		G		M		E		P		T		B
P		S		I		P	R	E	T	T	I	F	Y
S	E	N	T	I	N	E	L		I		L		U
U		E		A		E		O		L		N
G	R	A	N	U	L	E		B	E	N	G	A	L	I
A		L		M		B		X		A		O
R		T		B		A	U	T	O	B	A	H	N
C	L	E	A	R	C	U	T		E		L		O
A		R		E		T		R	E		N
N	E	E	D	L	E		E	X	I	G	E	N	C	Y
D		G		L		R		O		N		H
Y	E	O	M	A	N	R	Y		R	E	D	H	O	T

19

H	A	H	A		M	I	S	T	A	K	A	B	L	E
O		O			X		R		A		U		A
R	A	N	K		F	I	R	E	P	L	A	C	E	S
N		O		E		O		N		E		K		I
P	U	R	I	T	A	N	I	C		I	D	E	A	L
I		A		Y			H		D		T		Y
P	E	R	A	M	B	U	L	A	T	O	R			
E		Y		O		N		N		S		D	A
			B	L	U	E	S	T	O	C	K	I	N	G
A		J		O		A			O		L		R
S	L	A	N	G		R	E	C	A	P	T	U	R	E
S		M		I		T		O		E		T		E
A	T	M	O	S	P	H	E	R	E		M	I	N	I
Y		E		T		E		A			O		N
S	I	D	E	S	A	D	D	L	E		S	N	U	G

20

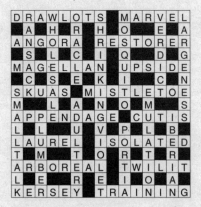

D	R	A	W	L	O	T	S		M	A	R	V	E	L
	A		H		R		H		O		E		A
A	N	G	O	R	A		R	E	S	T	O	R	E	R
	S		L		C		I		Q		D		G
M	A	G	E	L	L	A	N		U	P	S	I	D	E
	C		S		E		K		I		C		N
S	K	U	A	S		M	I	S	T	L	E	T	O	E
M		L		A		N		O		M		S
A	P	P	E	N	D	A	G	E		C	U	T	I	S
L		L		U		V		P		L		B
L	A	U	R	E	L		I	S	O	L	A	T	E	D
T		M		T		O		R		T		R
A	R	B	O	R	E	A	L		T	W	I	L	I	T
L		E		R		E		I		O		A
K	E	R	S	E	Y		T	R	A	I	N	I	N	G

21

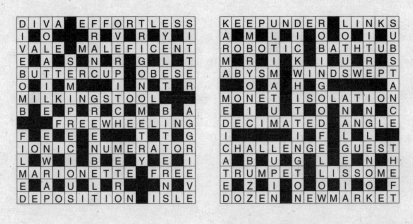

22

23

24

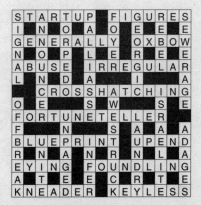

25

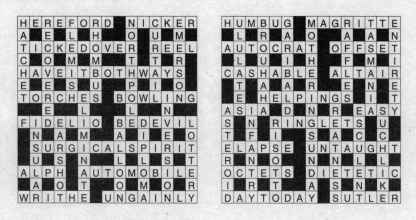

```
H E R E F O R D   N I C K E R
A   E   L   H   O   U   M
T I C K E D O V E R   R E E L
C   O   M   M   T   T   R
H A V E I T B O T H W A Y S
E   E   S   U   P   I   O
T O R C H E S   B O W L I N G
    E   L   L   N
F I D E L I O   B E D E V I L
  N   A   M   A   I   E   O
  S U R G I C A L S P I R I T
  U   S   N   L   L   S   T
A L P H   A U T O M O B I L E
A   O   T   O   M   O   R
W R I T H E   U N G A I N L Y
```

26

```
H U M B U G   M A G R I T T E
  L   R   A   O   A   A   N
A U T O C R A T   O F F S E T
L   U   I   H   F   M   I
C A S H A B L E   A L T A I R
T   A   A   R   E   N   E
E   H E L P I N G S   I   T
A S I A   D   N   R   E A S Y
S   N   R I N G L E T S   U
T   F   I   S   A   C   C
E L A P S E   U N T A U G H T
R   N   O   N   N   L   L
O C T E T S   D I E T E T I C
I   R   T   A   S   N   K
D A Y T O D A Y   S U T L E R
```

27

```
L A B O U R S A V I N G
A   A   P   A   I   O   T   P
D U S T C O V E R   B I H A R
D   S   O   E   T   E   E   O
E X O D U S   B U L L Y O F F
R   N   O   R   I
S A M I T E   E S S A Y I S T
  E   R   T   I   N   S
B E L L Y F U L   S T I T C H
A   O   R   I   E
R E D E S I G N   S P I D E R
Q   I   L   E   A   H   E   O
U N S A Y   N E X T O F K I N
E   T   P   E   O   N   K   R
  H E A V E N L Y B O D Y
```

28

```
K I N G F I S H E R   F E L L
R   E   I   P   Q   C   O
I M P E R V I O U S   T H U S
S   H   S   N   I   H   E   A
  W E L T   S I T W E L L O N
P   W   R   T   Y   I   O   G
U N S E E D E D   C R I N G E
N   F   R   F   A   L
C A M P U S   W A R P L A N E
H   O   S   V   I   P   D   S
D A M N A T I O N   A R M Y
R   B   L   V   T   R   I   B
U T A H   M A C E B E A R E R
N   S   C   S   N   A   A
K O A N   P E N T A T H L O N
```

29

```
P R I M A F A C I E · C A S T
· O · I · O · D · O · H
S C E N A R I O · I G N O R E
· K · K · S · L · C · S · E
· I N T E N T · A P T I T U D E
· R · H · N · A ·
M O O D · A U T O M O B I L E
· L · I N · A · L · A
C L O S E D B O O K · E T N A
· P · P · E · D
P O T A U F E U · S I P H O N
R · R · L · N · H · A · F
M I K A D O · T R I P L A N E
· B · T · R · I · F · M · O
C I T E · A V A N T G A R D E
```

30

```
F O R E A N D A F T · I C E D
A · E · C · E · R · H · A
W E A T H E R E Y E · S L U M
N · D · I B · I · S · O · A
· P L A Y I N G C A R D S
P · I · L · G · R · O · K
H O R S E W H I P · I N F E R
O · O · S · I · A · P · O O
T E N T H · T I N C T U R E S
O · M · E C · W · M · E
G L O B E T H E A T R E
E · N · L · C · P · I · L · B
N I G H · F O U R S T R O K E
I · E · C · I · E · K · R
C O R K · S K Y L A R K I N G
```

31

```
D U T C H · S U M M I N G U P
E · I · A · A · N · A U
P A L M I S T R Y · S C R U B
A · E · R · E · B · I · G · L
R E D U C E · G L A D I O L I
T · U · T · O · E · Y · C
M O N S T R O U S · R U L E R
E · A · N · S · E · E
N E R V E · G R O U N D S E L
T · C · N · U · M · O · A
S H I F T K E Y · E S P R I T
T · S · I · T · S · E · E · I
O N S E T · I N C O G N I T O
R · U · L · E · A · A · G · N
E A S T E N D E R · Y A N K S
```

32

```
S A F A R I P A R K · O S L O
W · A · I · O · E · E · V
A R T I C U L A T E · G A M E
Y · T · H · E · O · S · C · R
· W E S T · S T R I K E O U T
W · S · E · T · A · O · H
I N T E R V A L · S T O K E R
N · S · R · D · E · O
D E T A C H · D U M B S H O W
O · R · A · S · B · O · A · N
W H I R L P O O L · A R G O
S · C · E · U · I · R · G · W
H I K E · G R A N A D I L L A
O · L · · C · E · E · E · N
P E E R · T E R R O R I S E D
```

SOLUTIONS

33

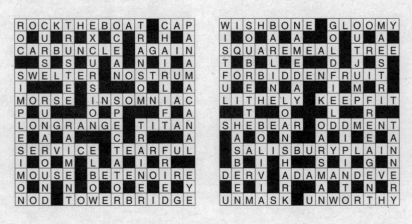

R	O	C	K	T	H	E	B	O	A	T		C	A	P
O		U		R		X		C		R		H		A
C	A	R	B	U	N	C	L	E		A	G	A	I	N
S			S		S		U		A		N		I	A
S	W	E	L	T	E	R		N	O	S	T	R	U	M
I			E		S		S		O		L		A	
M	O	R	S	E		I	N	S	O	M	N	I	A	C
P		U		O		P				F		A		A
L	O	N	G	R	A	N	G	E		T	I	T	A	N
E		A		A		C		R		A		A		A
S	E	R	V	I	C	E		T	E	A	R	F	U	L
I		O		M		L		A		I		R		
M	O	U	S	E		B	E	T	E	N	O	I	R	E
O		N		N		O		O		E		E		Y
N	O	D		T	O	W	E	R	B	R	I	D	G	E

34

W	I	S	H	B	O	N	E		G	L	O	O	M	Y
I		O		A		A		O		U		U		A
S	Q	U	A	R	E	M	E	A	L		T	R	E	E
T		B		L		E		D		J		S		
F	O	R	B	I	D	D	E	N	F	R	U	I	T	
U		E		N		A		I		M				R
L	I	T	H	E	L	Y		K	E	E	P	F	I	T
		T		O		L				R				
S	H	E	B	E	A	R		O	D	D	M	E	N	T
	A		O		N		A		I		E			A
	S	A	L	I	S	B	U	R	Y	P	L	A	I	N
	B		I		H		S		I		G			N
D	E	R	V		A	D	A	M	A	N	D	E	V	E
E		I	R		A		T		N		R			R
U	N	M	A	S	K		U	N	W	O	R	T	H	Y

35

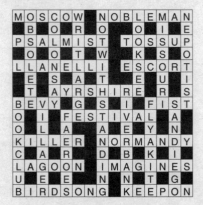

M	O	S	C	O	W		N	O	B	L	E	M	A	N
	B		O		R		O		O		I		E	
P	S	A	L	M	I	S	T		T	O	S	S	U	P
	O		O		T		W		K		S		O	
L	L	A	N	E	L	L	I		E	S	C	O	R	T
	E		S		A		T		E		U		I	
T		A	Y	R	S	H	I	R	E		R		S	
B	E	V	Y		G		S		I		F	I	S	T
O		I		F	E	S	T	I	V	A	L		A	
O		L		A		A		E		Y			N	
K	I	L	L	E	R		N	O	R	M	A	N	D	Y
C		A		R		D		B		K		I		
L	A	G	O	O	N		I	M	A	G	I	N	E	S
U		E		E		E		N		N		T		G
B	I	R	D	S	O	N	G		K	E	E	P	O	N

36

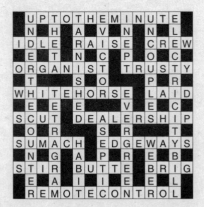

	U	P	T	O	T	H	E	M	I	N	U	T	E	
	N		H		A		V		N		N		L	
I	D	L	E		R	A	I	S	E		C	R	E	W
	E		T		N		C		P		O		C	
O	R	G	A	N	I	S	T		T	R	U	S	T	Y
	T			S		O			P		R			
W	H	I	T	E	H	O	R	S	E		L	A	I	D
	E		E		E		V		E		C			
S	C	U	T		D	E	A	L	E	R	S	H	I	P
	O		R		S		R							T
S	U	M	A	C	H		E	D	G	E	W	A	Y	S
	N		G		A		P		R		E		B	
S	T	I	R		B	U	T	T	E		B	R	I	G
	E		A		I		I		E		E		L	
	R	E	M	O	T	E	C	O	N	T	R	O	L	

37

38

39

40

SOLUTIONS

41

42

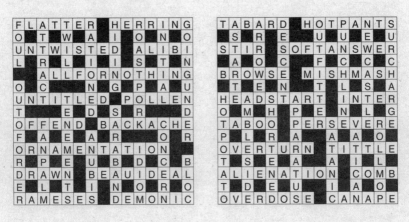

43

44

45

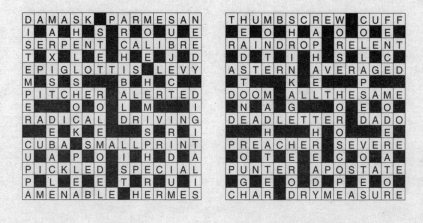

D	A	M	A	S	K		P	A	R	M	E	S	A	N
I		A		H		S		R		O		U		E
S	E	R	P	E	N	T		C	A	L	I	B	R	E
T		X		L		E		H		E		J		D
E	P	I	G	L	O	T	T	I	S		L	E	V	Y
M		S		S			B		H		C			
P	I	T	C	H	E	R		A	L	E	R	T	E	D
E				O		O		L		M				I
R	A	D	I	C	A	L		D	R	I	V	I	N	G
		E		K		E				S		R		I
C	U	B	A		S	M	A	L	L	P	R	I	N	T
U		A		P		O		I		H		D		A
P	I	C	K	L	E	D		S	P	E	C	I	A	L
P		L		E		E		T		R		U		I
A	M	E	N	A	B	L	E		H	E	R	M	E	S

46

T	H	U	M	B	S	C	R	E	W		C	U	F	F
	E		O		H		A		O		O		E	
R	A	I	N	D	R	O	P		R	E	L	E	N	T
	D		T		I		H		S		L		C	
A	S	T	E	R	N		A	V	E	R	A	G	E	D
			T		K		E		P					
D	O	O	M		A	L	L	T	H	E	S	A	M	E
	N		A		G		O		E		O			
D	E	A	D	L	E	T	T	E	R		D	A	D	O
			H				H		O		O			E
P	R	E	A	C	H	E	R		S	E	V	E	R	E
	O		T		E		E		C		O		A	
P	U	N	T	E	R		A	P	O	S	T	A	T	E
	G		E		O		D		P		E		O	
C	H	A	R		D	R	Y	M	E	A	S	U	R	E

47

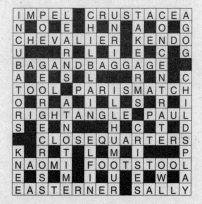

I	M	P	E	L		C	R	U	S	T	A	C	E	A
N		O		E		H		N		A		O		G
C	H	E	V	A	L	I	E	R		K	E	N	D	O
U		R		L		I		E		C		G		G
B	A	G	A	N	D	B	A	G	G	A	G	E		
A		E		S		L		R		N		C		
T	O	O	L		P	A	R	I	S	M	A	T	C	H
O		R		A		I		L		S		R		I
R	I	G	H	T	A	N	G	L	E		P	A	U	L
S		E		N		H		C	T	D				D
		C	L	O	S	E	Q	U	A	R	T	E	R	S
K		R		T		L	M		I					P
N	A	O	M	I		F	O	O	T	S	T	O	O	L
E		S		M		I	U		E		W		A	
E	A	S	T	E	R	N	E	R		S	A	L	L	Y

48

P	I	S	C	E	S		W	A	L	K	O	V	E	R
	N		A		T		E		N		A		A	
K	E	E	L	H	A	U	L		B	A	L	L	A	D
	Q		I		I		L		V		E		I	
J	U	N	G	F	R	A	U		L	E	A	N	T	O
	I		U		C		P		R		C		H	
T		L	E	A	T	H	E	R	Y		I		A	
M	Y	R	A		S		O	A		C	A	L	M	
E		A		W	E	L	L	N	I	G	H		I	
A		M		H		S		N		A		N		
S	I	S	K	I	N		T	U	C	K	S	H	O	P
U		H		T		E		L		U		L		
R	O	O	K	I	E		R	O	O	T	B	E	E	R
E		M		S		E		U		L		U		
S	H	E	P	H	E	R	D		D	R	E	A	M	T

SOLUTIONS

49

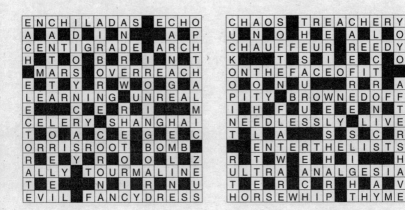

50

51

52

53

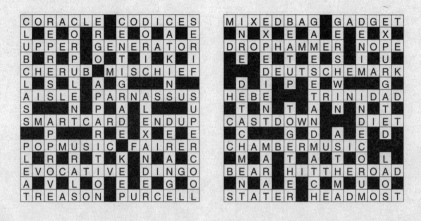

54

55

56

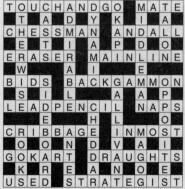

SOLUTIONS

57

```
P U N J A B   M A C H E A T H
N   A   E   U   I   N   E
A F F R I G H T   C R A T E R
  A   N   G   A   S   I   I
M I S D E A L T   P U L P I T
  R   Y   R   I   T   O   A
  L   C A M P S I T E   P   G
H Y P E   A   M   R   H E B E
I   L   I N S U L A T E   R
G   A   T   T   D   P   U
H I T M A N   A B E T T I N G
B   O   L   N   M   A   E
A U N T I E   D R A U G H T Y
L   I   A   I   R   O   T
L O C H N E S S   K E N N E L
```

58

```
M A R R I A G E B U R E A U
U   A   C   R   I   E   B   D
S H I R T L E S S   C H A I R
T   M   U   E   Q   E   N   O
A V E R S   T R U M P E D U P
R   N   I   E   T   O   I
D E T H R O N E   F I N N A N
P   E   G   P   O   T
L E A R N T   C L A N N I S H
A   Q   D   R   U   S   E
S A U C E P A N S   T O R S O
T   A   R   N   H   O   A   C
E N V O I   C L I E N T E L E
R   I   N   I   E   I   L   A
  S T A G E D I R E C T I O N
```

59

```
F A S T   P A R R   B E D I M
A   U   C   G   E   Y   E   A
R E P R O V E   C A R T O O N
A   E   L   N   O   E   D   A
W O R D O R D E R   T R O U T
A   R   A   D   U   R   E
Y E S M A N   D E C R E A S E
  N   D   B   R   N   N
L O O K O V E R   K O W T O W
E   W   B   H   B   F   R
G A B L E   E X E M P L A R Y
A   O   E   A   H   O   B   N
T R U S T E D   A S S U A G E
E   N   L   E   V   T   T   C
S I D L E   D U E L   P E R K
```

60

```
H E A D O N   B I R D S E Y E
  X   E   I   N   E   N   L
S O A P   G E T T H E B I R D
  T   L   H   H   P   G   E
W I S E N T   B E S S E M E R
  C   T   I   C   P   A   S
C A F E T E R I A   A I T C H
U   R   R   E   R   C   I   I
P I E C E   B U T T E R C U P
I   E   B   E   A   A   T
D E V O U T L Y   P O M P O M
S   E   C   L   S   P   P
B I R T H R I G H T   A X I S
O   S   E   O   E   R   A
W R E S T I N G   R O T U N D
```

61

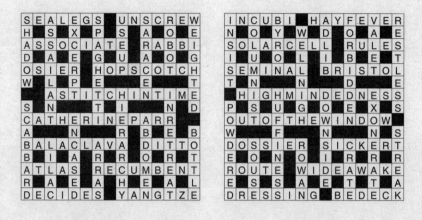

```
S E A L E G S   U N S C R E W
H   S   X   P   S   A   O   E
A S S O C I A T E   R A B B I
D   A   E   G   U   A   O   G
O S I E R   H O P S C O T C H
W   L   P   E   E   R   T   T
    A S T I T C H I N T I M E
S   N   T   I   N   N   D
C A T H E R I N E P A R R
A   N   R   B   E   B
B A L A C L A V A   D I T T O
B   I   A   R   R   O   R   T
A T L A S   R E C U M B E N T
R   A   E   A   H   E   A   L
D E C I D E S   Y A N G T Z E
```

62

```
I N C U B I   H A Y F E V E R
N   O   Y   W   D   O   A   E
S O L A R C E L L   R U L E S
I   U   O   L   I   B   E   T
S E M I N A L   B R I S T O L
T   N   N   N   D   E
  H I G H M I N D E D N E S S
P   S   U   G   O   E X   S
O U T O F T H E W I N D O W
W   F   N   N   N   S
D O S S I E R   S I C K E R T
E   O   N   O   I   R   R   R
R O U T E   W I D E A W A K E
E   S   S   A   E   T   T   A
D R E S S I N G   B E D E C K
```

63

```
W A L L S H A V E E A R S
E   I   A   C   N   R   H   B
L O N G F A C E D   T R O L L
T   K   E   U   G   Y   W   A
A S S E T   S L A P   O T I C
N   Y   E   M   C   R   K
S C H O L A R   E G O T I S M
C   A   A   A   R   A   A
H A N G M A N   T I D D L E R
A   D   P   O   E   O   K
U N I T   G R I N   N O R S E
U   W   P   F   S   B   E   T
N O O S E   O R I F L A M M E
G   R   R   L   L   E   I   E
  K N U C K L E D U S T E R
```

64

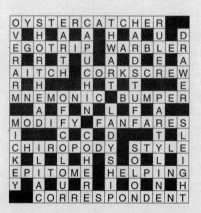

```
O Y S T E R C A T C H E R
V   H   A   A   H   A   U   D
E G O T R I P   W A R B L E R
R   R   T   U   A   D   E   A
A I T C H   C O R K S C R E W
R   H   H   T   T   E
M N E M O N I C   B U M P E R
  A   F   N   L   F   A
M O D I F Y   F A N F A R E S
I   C   C   D   T   L
C H I R O P O D Y   S T Y L E
K   L   L   H   S   O   L   I
E P I T O M E   H E L P I N G
Y   A   U   R   I   O   N   H
  C O R R E S P O N D E N T
```

SOLUTIONS

65

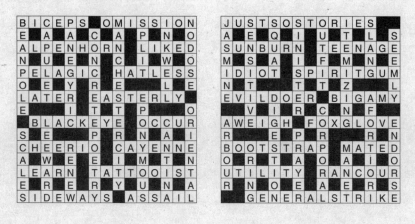

B	I	C	E	P	S			O	M	I	S	S	I	O	N
E		A		A		C		A		P		N			O
A	L	P	E	N	H	O	R	N		L	I	K	E	D	
N		U		E		N		C		I		W			O
P	E	L	A	G	I	C		H	A	T	L	E	S	S	
O		E		Y		R		E		L			L		E
L	A	T	E	R		E	A	S	T	E	R	L	Y		
E			I		T		T		P			O	
	B	L	A	C	K	E	Y	E		O	C	C	U	R
S		E		P		R		N		A			I
C	H	E	E	R	I	O		C	A	Y	E	N	N	E
A		W		E		E		I		M		T	
L	E	A	R	N		T	A	T	T	O	O	I	S	T
E		R		E	R		Y		U		N		A
S	I	D	E	W	A	Y	S		A	S	S	A	I	L

66

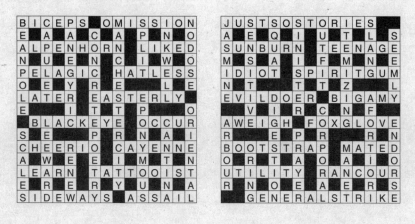

J	U	S	T	S	O	S	T	O	R	I	E	S	
A		E		Q		I		U		T		L		S
S	U	N	B	U	R	N		T	E	E	N	A	G	E
M		S		A		I		F		M		N		E
I	D	I	O	T		S	P	I	R	I	T	G	U	M
N		T		T		T		Z					L
E	V	I	L	D	O	E	R		B	I	G	A	M	Y
		V		I		R		C		N		F	
A	W	E	I	G	H		F	O	X	G	L	O	V	E
R			E		P		R			R		R		N
B	O	O	T	S	T	R	A	P		M	A	T	E	D
O		R		T		A		O		A		I		O
U	T	I	L	I	T	Y		R	A	N	C	O	U	R
R		N		O		E		A		E		R		S
	G	E	N	E	R	A	L	S	T	R	I	K	E

67

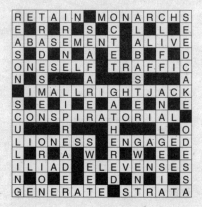

R	E	T	A	I	N		M	O	N	A	R	C	H	S
E		R		R		S		C		L		L		E
A	B	A	S	E	M	E	N	T		A	L	I	V	E
S		D		N		A		E		B		F		D
O	N	E	S	E	L	F		T	R	A	F	F	I	C
N		S		A		S			S				C
	I	M	A	L	L	R	I	G	H	T	J	A	C	K
S		E		I		E		A		E		N		E
C	O	N	S	P	I	R	A	T	O	R	I	A	L	
U			R		H			L		O	
L	I	O	N	E	S	S		E	N	G	A	G	E	D
L		R		A		W		R		W		E		E
I	L	I	A	D		E	L	E	V	E	N	S	E	S
N		O		E		E		D		N		I		S
G	E	N	E	R	A	T	E		S	T	R	A	T	A

68

J	I	T	T	E	R	B	U	G		C	L	A	N	G
E		R		X		E		E		L		R		L
T	H	I	S	T	L	E		N	A	U	T	I	L	I
T		U		E		R		E		M		E		S
Y	E	M	E	N			A	C	R	O	P	O	L	I	S
		V		S		N		A					A
S	C	I	F	I		D	A	L	M	A	T	I	A	N
A		R		O		S		P		U		L		D
S	P	I	N	N	A	K	E	R		S	A	L	V	O
S			I			A		T		J	
E	N	I	G	M	A	T	I	C		R	O	U	N	D
N		N		A		T		T		A		D		E
A	N	T	H	I	L	L		I	L	L	E	G	A	L
C		E		Z		E		C		I		E		V
H	O	R	D	E		S	K	E	D	A	D	D	L	E

69

```
A B O V E S U S P I C I O N
I   L   N   O   H   U   T
R E D H A N D E D   R E T I E
I   M   T   U   I   R   A
N O O S E   L O U I S I A N A
G   O   A   M   T   G   N
C O N F E T T I   I M P E N D
U   N   E   R   A       S
P L A N T S   P O S S I B L Y
B   N   R   S   U   I   M
O N T H E N A I L   A C T U P
A   O   N   P   E   V   A
R O N D O   E X T R O V E R T
D   I   U   L   T   I   R
  R O S S D E P E N D E N C Y
```

70

```
U N M O V E D   A M U S I N G
G   U   I   O   C   N   C   E
L I G H T S O U T   C H E A T
Y   S   A   M   I   E   P   K
  H A L F S O V E R E I G N
H   O   D   E   T   C   O
I N T E G R A L   J A C K E T
G   U   Y   M   I       T
H A G G I S   P I N N A C L E
S   A   T   F   N   R   D
E X T R A O R D I N A R Y
A   E   R   I   S   F   W   M
S A L M I   A S T R O L O G Y
O   E   S   R   E   O   L   R
N I G H T L Y   R A T A F I A
```

71

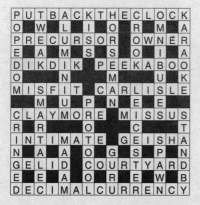

```
P U T B A C K T H E C L O C K
O   W   L   I   O   R   M   A
P R E C U R S O R   O W N E R
E   A   M   S   S   O   I   A
D I K D I K   P E E K A B O O
O   N   M       U   K
M I S F I T   C A R L I S L E
    M   U   P   N   E   E
C L A Y M O R E   M I S S U S
R   R   O   C   T
I N T I M A T E   G E I S H A
N   A   A   O   G   S   P   N
G E L I D   C O U R T Y A R D
E   E   A   O   R   E   W   B
D E C I M A L C U R R E N C Y
```

72

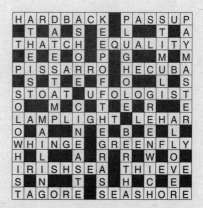

```
H A R D B A C K   P A S S U P
  T   A   S   E   L   T   A
T H A T C H   E Q U A L I T Y
  E   E   O   P   G   M   M
P I S S A R R O   H E C U B A
  S   T   E   F   O   L   S
S T O A T   U F O L O G I S T
O   M   C   T   E   R   E
L A M P L I G H T   L E H A R
O   A   N   E   B   E   L
W H I N G E   G R E E N F L Y
H   L   A   R   R   W   O
I R I S H S E A   T H I E V E
S   N   T   S   H   C   E
T A G O R E   S E A S H O R E
```

SOLUTIONS

73

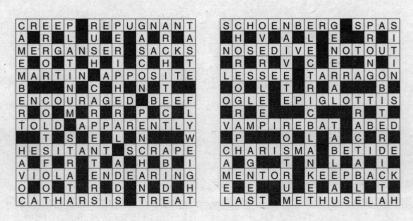

```
C R E E P · R E P U G N A N T
A · R · L · U · E · A R · A
M E R G A N S E R · S A C K S
E · O · T · H · I C H · T
M A R T I N · A P P O S I T E
B · N · C · H · N · T
E N C O U R A G E D · B E E F
R · O · M · R · R · P C · L
T O L D · A P P A R E N T L Y
· T · S E L · N · W
H E S I T A N T · S C R A P E
A · F · R · T · A H B · I
V I O L A · E N D E A R I N G
O · O · T · R · D · N D H
C A T H A R S I S · T R E A T
```

74

```
S C H O E N B E R G · S P A S
· H · V A · L E · R · I
N O S E D I V E · N O T O U T
· R · R V · C E · N · I
L E S S E E · T A R R A G O N
· O · L · T R A · A · B
O G L E · E P I G L O T T I S
· R · E · C · R · T
V A M P I R E B A T · A B E D
· P · O · L A C · R
C H A R I S M A · B E T I D E
A · G · T · N L A · I
M E N T O R · K E E P B A C K
E · E · U E · A · L T
L A S T · M E T H U S E L A H
```

75

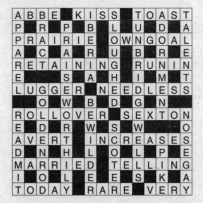

```
A B B E · K I S S · T O A S T
P · R · P · B · L U · D · A
P R A I R I E · O W N G O A L
A · C · A R · U · B R · E
R E T A I N I N G · R U N I N
E · · S A · H I · M · T
L U G G E R · N E E D L E S S
· O · W · B D G · N
R O L L O V E R · S E X T O N
E · D · R · W S W · · O
A V E R T · I N C R E A S E S
D · N · H · L O · L P · E
M A R R I E D · T E L L I N G
I · O · L · E E · S K · A
T O D A Y · R A R E · V E R Y
```

76

```
L I B R A · S E N T E N C E D
O · A · L · T E · U · O · U
C O R K S C R E W · L A M E D
K · · A · E E · O P · S
S A L E C A T A L O G U E · ·
M · I · E C · · I T · M
I O T A · C H O R U S L I N E
T · T · M E E · E T · R
H E L I O G R A P H · L I A R
S · E · N · A R · O · Y
· W H A T D O Y O U K N O W
E · O · L · I · M M · · I
T E M P I · S H E E P F O L D
C · E · S · C N · U · A · O
H A N G A B O U T · S T R A W
```

77

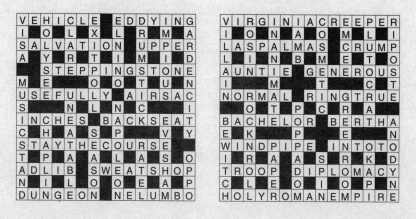

```
V E H I C L E   E D D Y I N G
I   O   L   X   L   R   M   A
S A L V A T I O N   U P P E R
A   Y   R   T   I   M   I   D
M   S T E P P I N G S T O N E
M   E   O   O   T   U   N
U S E F U L L Y   A I R S A C
S   N   L   N   C       I
I N C H E S   B A C K S E A T
C   H   A   S   P   V   Y
S T A Y T H E C O U R S E
T   P   A   A   L   A   S   O
A D L I B   S W E A T S H O P
N   I   L   O   O   E   A   P
D U N G E O N   N E L U M B O
```

78

```
V I R G I N I A C R E E P E R
I   O   N   A   O   M   L   I
L A S P A L M A S   C R U M P
L   I   N   B   M   E   T   O
A U N T I E   G E N E R O U S
I   I   M   T   C   T
N O R M A L   R I N G T R U E
O   T   P   C   R   A
B A C H E L O R   B E R T H A
E   K   P   P   E       N
W I N D P I P E   I N T O T O
I   R   A   S   R   K   D
T R O O P   D I P L O M A C Y
C   L   E   O   I   P   N
H O L Y R O M A N E M P I R E
```

79

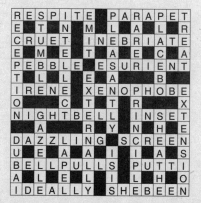

```
R E S P I T E   P A R A P E T
E   T   N   M   L   A   L   R
C R U E T   I N E B R I A T E
E   M   E   T   A   E   C   A
P E B B L E   E S U R I E N T
T   L   L   E   A   B
I R E N E   X E N O P H O B E
O   C   T   T   R   X
N I G H T B E L L   I N S E T
    A   R   Y   N   H   E
D A Z Z L I N G   S C R E E N
U   E   A   A   I   I   A   S
B E L L P U L L S   P U T T I
A   L   E   L   I   L   H   O
I D E A L L Y   S H E B E E N
```

80

```
S A V E O N E S B A C O N
T   I   R   M   R   A   E   B
E N C L A S P   A P P A R E L
W   A   C   H   I   A   V   I
A R R A Y   A B S O R B E N T
R   I   S   E   I       H
D O O R N A I L   E S C A P E
    U   E   S   B   O   D
D I S O W N   T R A N S M I T
E   F   P   A   I   R
C U S T O D I A N   P A S T A
I   C   R   G   D   R   S   P
D I O C E S E   I D O L I S E
E   T   S   O   S   O   O   Z
    S I T O N T H E F E N C E
```